THE MAGIC OF THE ANIMALS

THE MAGIC OF THE ANIMALS

Patrizia
Krachmalnicoff

TRANSLATED BY
SUE NEWSON-SMITH
WITH ILLUSTRATIONS BY
PAT HANNAH

Arlington Books
Clifford Street Mayfair
London

THE MAGIC OF THE ANIMALS
First published 1977 by
Arlington Books (Publishers) Ltd
3 Clifford Street Mayfair
London W.1

© SugarCo Milan 1975
English translation
© Arlington Books 1977
Illustrations
© Arlington Books 1977

Made and printed in England by
The Garden City Press Limited
London and Letchworth

ISBN 85140 · 259 · 3

CONTENTS

Acknowledgements

Grateful acknowledgement is made to:

Gerald Durrell for permission to use extracts from THE STATIONARY ARK, *published by Collins Publishers.*

Rowena Farr for permission to use extracts from SEAL MORNING, *published by Hutchinson & Company.*

Introduction

'Magic' is a fashionable word today and as a result is frequently over-used, so that it often gets away from its original and basic meaning.

The dictionary defines 'magic' as the 'art of performing miracles with spells' – an ability reserved to a few who are gifted with exceptional powers, and who can accomplish actions that most other men regard as impossible and which religion labels as miraculous.

Religious beliefs apart, the only difference between magic and miracles is that to accomplish a miracle those undertaking it need to use all their will-power while magic demands the tools of the trade, like philtres, powders and potions. But this is a generalisation and naturally there are exceptions in this field as in every other.

Given this premise then, what does the title 'Magic of Animals' mean? For the sake of argument (but not my argument) let us suppose that in absolute terms, animals are inferior to men. Magic must then be the faculty some animals possess for accomplishing actions which generally only a man is capable of achieving. But if we stick to this definition, we will see that so-called 'magicians' are infinitely more numerous among lower animals than humans, and that some of their magic spells occur so frequently and with such intensity that they really do merit the label of 'ability' and should be acknowledged by formal science as well as animal lovers.

But there is another kind of animal magic which is far more unorthodox than the term we are using: it is the sentimental, aesthetic magic which can create a particular state of mind.

In the way we speak of the magic of a sunset or a seascape or whatever natural spectacle we find particularly impressive, I think we can also speak of the magic of a kitten purring, even though there is nothing supernatural about that, or of Charlie Brown's warm puppy, welcoming you on the doorstep, or a horse galloping along the river bank, or a coloured humming bird which is so tiny that you can hold it in the palm of your hand.

But it is wrong to limit ourselves to graceful creatures alone. Every animal has its own brand of magic. Even the ungainly and ugly warthog or the hippopotomus can make some tenderness stir within us.

Since this type of magic is not triggered off by aesthetic or intellectual gifts alone, each animal must have its own particular qualities which make it an individual and unique and recognisable among all the others, if one has the desire to find out and the patience to concern oneself with them for a time.

This is what I mean by the 'magic of animals' – not in an exclusively scientific sense but also empirically and emotionally, although taking everything science has discovered and established into account.

For many people, the world of animals is completely without interest unless it has some gastronomic or hunting value. This magic of animals is not for them.

Only those who, like me, have lived with animals for a long time and learned to love and respect them and to do their best to understand them, will understand what I mean by this 'magic'.

SVPERSTITION AND MYTH

Sir Kitcham

CHAPTER 1

Superstition and Myth

Since time immemorial animals have been in perpetual contact with man and have been subject to their observation and, rather visibly, to their lack of comprehension. Primitive man had no other model outside himself and could not help but find animal behaviour strange, incomprehensible and mysterious, and so made animals the object of his beliefs and of his most absurd superstitions.

Naturally, certain superstitions which grew up later were probably due to a single incident which happened to an important person, or to a curious coincidence which became built into the system by somebody or event, and therefore vary from country to country.

In India, for example, where the population has remained largely primitive, the most varied superstitions and legends abound, especially about the commonest animals. It is strange that such people, living primarily in conditions of misery and perpetual starvation, are the ones who obstinately protect and worship certain animals which they could quite easily eat but whose slaughter is most severely punished.

This law also applies to tourists. Two years ago, some friends of mine had an unhappy experience while crossing India in a Volkswagen van. They had a minor collison with a cow that was wandering around the streets of Bombay and had to pay a large fine and escape extremely fast to avoid being lynched by the crowd. But as they were leaving, they just managed to hear a policeman warn them that if the incident occurred a second time, they would land up in prison and if it happened a third time, they would be condemned to death.

Of course, such events please animal-lovers the world over, however absurd and anachronistic it might be for sacred cows to wander unrestricted through the streets of a city full of the chaotic traffic which is so common in eastern countries.

In Madeira, on the other hand, dogs and cats are not sacred but dearly loved and it is strictly forbidden to allow them to wander around the streets on their own, precisely for fear that they might be run over.

But let us return to India where the legends and superstitions are particularly interesting, especially those about monkeys which are regarded as having supernatural powers – possibly through their behavioural similarity to man. Primitive people regard this behaviour and physical similarity as a divine quality and therefore deify those possessing it.

One of the native gods, Hanuman, is a monkey-god and legend tells how an army of monkeys came to his aid and attacked his enemies. This episode is often depicted in paintings and local sculptures. The famous god, Rama, was helped by a band of monkeys to recover his wife who had been stolen by the enemy, and the chain of small islands which links the two larger islands east of Ceylon is supposed to be a bridge built by monkeys in far-off days to help Rama cross.

In the Himalayas, there is a mountain peak called Bandar Punckh which means 'monkey's tail'. Every year a single monkey is said to climb to the summit on his own and stay there in absolute isolation, until another monkey relieves him at the end of the year. No one knows the reason for this isolation – perhaps meditation – given the proximity of the wide variety of monasteries found in these parts. At any rate two curious facts stand out: first, no one has yet checked to see whether there really is a monkey up there on the peak and secondly, just for once, this is a 'neutral' legend with no good or evil attached to it.

Stories about Macaque monkeys, which are very common in India and considered sacred and untouchable despite their particularly treacherous nature, are the complete opposite.

One of the most absurd legends, which has not yet been confirmed, is that they form armies with officers, sentries and guards and make proper military sorties. What Indians universally recognise is their extremely spiteful and decidedly intractable nature.

In certain parts of India when a wedding takes place, the head of the household will place a turban outside the door, a suit, some fruit and also some nuts for any monkey who might happen along and wish to take part in the ceremony. This is to show that these touchy animals have not been forgotten, rather like the bad fairy who was not invited to the princess's christening. If monkeys are offended by not being invited, legend says they will break into the house, destroy everything and ruin the wedding.

At Benares, one of the ritual acts at a temple dedicated to the monkey-god, consists of feeding the monkeys which live round about. In addition, these legends are nearly always linked with religion.

There are everyday superstitions concerning monkeys which correspond to ours – such as not walking under a ladder or setting out on a journey on Friday the 13th.

For example, monkeys' bones are supposed to bring good luck and one must not build a house where they have been found. Building work will be beset by difficulties in places where a lot of monkeys are living.

If you mention the word 'monkey' in your conversation in

the morning, it means you will have nothing to eat all day, but you can avoid this by calling a monkey a 'tree climber'. On the other hand, if you stare a monkey in the face it brings you good fortune.

In Assam once a year, a monkey is sacrificed to protect the population from illness and accidents throughout the year. Conditions in India do not seem to corroborate this theory but it is easy to see how the indigenous population cannot easily separate themselves from their convictions. Perhaps they think that if they did not make this sacrifice, their conditions would be even worse. But legends and superstitions about monkeys are not a prerogative of India alone. They occur in all countries where they exist because of their great similarity to man.

One African tribe believes there is an affinity between monkeys and pairs of twins and the latter are never allowed to eat monkey meat. If a hunter brings home the corpse of a monkey, the parents of the twins will beat it with cudgels so that all the monkeys in the forest will sense their disapproval.

The strangest legend comes from Java where a plant grows which is poisonous for men but not for monkeys. Only young men who have heard a buffalo's bellow can eat this plant with safety, but first they have to imitate a monkey so that the plant will believe they are monkeys. It is not clear how the plant knows whether those who are imitating monkeys have heard the buffalo's cry or not.

The Japanese are well supplied with monkeys also but are more poetic and without so many superstitions. In compensation they are rich in tales in which monkeys are portrayed as wily, malign and wicked. It is not known whether this is due to their similarity to man, but it is probable. The Japanese too have their own sacred monkeys linked to Koshin, the god of the road. These are the three most famous monkeys in the world – Mazaru, Kilazaru and Iwazaru, who have been sculpted in ivory, bronze and wood and see nothing, hear nothing and say nothing. They are found on the roadsides and are often given offerings.

In New Guinea, it is believed that the souls of the dead pass into monkeys who, as a result, become untouchable. A similar belief exists in Cornwall and Devon, notoriously lacking in monkeys but teeming with seagulls, which the fishermen will not kill because they believe they contain the souls of drowned fishermen.

Does this sort of belief exist in India? Apparently not, since every superstition there is a good one and certainly not cheap. In an Indian village called Deshnoke, which suffers constantly from famine, a marble temple has been dedicated to mice. This is not so bad because although marble costs a lot it cannot be eaten. But the most incredible thing is that this perenially starved people feed thousands of 'sacred' mice with grain which they use to make bread and serve it to the mice on silver platters, maintaining that the souls of the dead live on in mice.

Touring the world, you will discover that the souls of the dead choose a wide variety of animal bodies to live in.

In Fez, in Morocco, there was a hospital for storks until a few years ago, where every good Moroccan would take wounded storks. This is not to say that Moroccans are animal-lovers, or indeed stork lovers, but the reason lies in a tenet of the Islamic faith which prescribes that once in a lifetime, a Muslim must visit the tomb of the great Saint in Fez. And a popular superstition has been added saying that those who do not accomplish this during their lifetime will return as storks after their death to undertake the pilgrimage to the Saint's tomb. So, whenever a Muslim spots a stork in Fez, he recognises the souls of his co-religionists and gives it assistance.

Back in India, religion forbids the killing of the ten thousand remaining elephants in existence, despite their rich source of ivory. White hunters who are decimating elephants should consider this because it will soon be necessary to decree that killing is forbidden on ecological grounds to save the species from the danger of extinction.

In Australia, strange legends surround the dugong, a mermaid-like marine animal similar to the seal. The Australians' fear of them is justified because the female of the species often appears standing upright in the water, holding its baby between its fins in such a human pose that, from afar, it gives the impression of a woman and her child standing on the water.

In South-West Africa, the Bushmen worship the praying mantis because the position of its back claws reminds them of people praying. In Honolulu, the moonfish is so rare that if one is caught it is immediately thrown back into the sea. The Hawaiians look on it as the god of all mackerel and sardines in the sea and it is therefore sacriligious to kill it.

The frog is certainly not one of the animals that shines through in popular superstition, even though it has its own magical functions in the Orinoco. When a young girl is looking for a husband, the witchdoctor takes a frog, feeds it up for 30 days, then kneels before it entreating it to find a husband for the girl. If, at the end of 3 days, the eventual lover has not appeared, the frog is no longer fed.

After a further 3 days, the witchdoctor threatens and curses the frog. After another 3 days, it is set free with the philosophical comment: "We were mistaken, frog."

Perhaps all girls seeking a husband should adopt this custom, although 39 days is not many in which to find a husband. If this tribe continues using this method, it must work sometimes. It is almost too obvious to mention but it is a far more difficult method for city girls compared to country girls, due to the scarcity of frogs in the cities.

Let us travel back to ancient Egypt and discuss the animal which was ignored and rejected by the most idolatrous of people – the pig. The Egyptians adored and worshipped every animal but the pig. This extremely fanatical and religious people continually forced men into temples, but always found excuses to keep out pigherdsmen and kept them well away, as pigs were considered unclean.

However, a more benevolent tradition towards pigs, although of unknown origin, is the one which advises insomniacs to tie a sow to the end of their beds in order to get to sleep.

We will also travel back to ancient Rome where it was believed that a hyena's skin made warriors invincible. Seeing the importance armies had in Roman times, this uncongenial and unloved animal gloried at least in some satisfaction. Still in Rome, we find that Cato, the censor, maintained that the only way to get over an illness was to hold a swallow in one's hand, and touch the ill parts of the body with it, while singing a nursery rhyme.

We may laugh at the simple-minded superstitions of people distant from us in tradition and culture, but we will laugh on the other side of our faces when we look at superstitions nearer our own comfortable civilisation, which risk involving us – for instance, the thirteen people round the dinner table, the step-ladder in the street, the gift of a handkerchief, partings on Fridays – these are still joked about lightly and passed over by most people who are perhaps laughing at themselves. But there is worse in this civilisation when we sometimes find ourselves going backwards and taking up buried and forgotten uses again. It was only recently discovered that there was a fresh epidemic of black magic rites in which animals, their blood, limbs and guts, play a basic part. The Black Masses of Satanists specify that it is essential to cut a cockerel's throat in order to call up the devil. The cockerel is today's substitute for the first-born child so tranquilly slaughtered by the Marchioness of Montespan during the reign of the Sun King.

Books like *Rosemary's Baby* and others clearly show that however much one imagines these kind of things have died down, people appear to be thinking about them more and more.

But let us pass on to less bloodthirsty things. In the Vosges today, people still believe that a black chicken born on a Good Friday is essential in practising witchcraft and can also make people invisible. Again, we must ask ourselves: how is it that people go on believing such things especially when no one has ever been made invisible? The answer can only be that for hundreds of years, no black chickens have ever been born on a Good Friday, and that this old tradition is maintained through lack of proof to contradict it.

The commonest animal superstitions in every country are those surrounding birds like owls and hoopoes who are unattractive and generally considered to be bad omens. One positive belief regarding the screech owl is that it brings good luck to the house it settles on. But this is immediately counter balanced by the fact that it brings bad luck to the house it stares at. While the hoopoe can boast of many literary references from great writers and poets, other humbler birds are feared by city folk who mostly ignore them while country folk know that they are extremely useful and valuable exterminators of harmful insects.

In Utah, one of the states of modern and go-ahead America, a law is still in existence dating from 1848, which lays down extremely severe punishment for people who kill seagulls. It was put on the statute book in 1848 when an invasion of locusts destroyed an entire harvest and the crops of the Mormon community. Every attempt to stop the locusts proved useless and people resigned themselves to it, when a huge number of seagulls suddenly descended and destroyed all the locusts. The seagulls were thought to have been sent from Providence and since that day have been protected and declared untouchable.

We come finally to the most interesting animal from a superstitious point of view: the cat. We see them everywhere and practically consider them to be one of the family. In Europe, in fact, since the beginning of civilisation, cats were considered beings from the shadows with powers akin to those of the devil. Today, in some particularly backward villages, it seems that people still believe cats turn into devils in the seventh year.

As everyone knows the continent over, Europeans believe black cats bring bad luck, especially when they cross the road. It is particularly interesting therefore, to find that in England, which has never considered itself European, this superstition has been turned inside out: for the English a cat brings good luck especially if it is black and even more so when it crosses the road. Beyond Europe, since the end of antiquity, cats have enjoyed an enviable existence. Domesticated by the Chinese about 5,000 years ago, cats have also always been loved and protected by Muslims, while the Egyptians worshipped them and regarded killing them as a crime far more serious than manslaughter.

People who still consider the cat sacred today in some ways are the Indians. In Akola, people who kill cats are obliged to substitute a solid gold one which is then thrown into the sea. It is strange how the poorest people often have the costliest superstitions.

The only people who always agree about cats are sailors the world over. Everyone knows sailors are a race apart in which the different nationalities disappear and dissolve into the larger community of the sea.

Every sailor in the world has always considered a cat on board ship to be good luck. When a ship is wrecked, the cat is always one of the first to be saved, although it is not known whether they go before or after the women and children. There are very old superstitions about cats on board ship: if they miaow incessantly the ship will have a bad voyage; if they frolic about, then there will be a fair wind; if you wish the wind to change, all you have to do is to put the cat under a saucepan in the galley; and finally, if a cat falls overboard by accident a furious storm will immediately blow up.

To finish with cats, here is the simplest explanation of the popularly-held belief that if a cat washes behind its ears, it means it is going to rain. This is true in that the nerves on the back paws of a cat relax when the weather changes for the worse and they manage to reach behind their ears with their hind legs which they cannot normally do.

Turning to 'bad' superstitions, in particular the belief that cats were devil's familiars, we know that in the Middle Ages, it was considered honourable to kill cats with one's bare hands. The Emperor Frederick II conferred a knighthood on a certain Kircham, who killed three cats, not just with his hands but also by biting them.

Towards the end of the seventeenth century, the Inquisition which continually searched for fresh motives for more public burnings, condemned to death people suspected of maintaining the ancient veneration for cats, and accused them of witchcraft.

In connection with this, we cannot omit the trials suffered by animals in the Middle Ages, of which we still have evidence. It is extremely interesting to examine such ancient trials and the frequency with which they occurred. One law historian catalogued as many as two hundred in one century. The causes can be traced back to the ancient belief that certain animals were the incarnation of the devil – a belief that was taken to extremes in the Middle Ages and the Inquisition. But even if the mania for fire and torture can be partly attributed to religious fanaticism, it is also the result of a taste for strong sensations, a predilection for black and white, good and evil, which is one of the principal characteristics of the Middle Ages.

So it came about that pigs, which often kill their first-born were mutilated before being killed and that rabid dogs were progressively tortured and mutilated according to the number of people they had bitten, beginning with their paws, and their ears, and then the tail, finishing off with their claws. They were looked on as assassins, because people could not picture rabies as an illness.

To extort hypothetical confessions from animals, the same instruments of torture were often used on animals as for men, and the howls of pain from the poor animals were considered admissions of guilt.

As often as not in these cases, the spirit of modernism rebelled, being unable to see in these monstrous acts, anything other than unleashed cruelty, perversion and bad faith which was often disguised as religion, or worse, sometimes the law. Animals which were the most tortured and which used to wander freely through the streets were pigs. Always being hungry, they grew fierce and slaughtered their first-born. Other animals accused were bulls, which were frequently stoned to death and horses, whose only fault, apart from being highly-bred and sprightly, was that they were thought to be possessed by the devil and were therefore burned alive. This continued until the end of the eighteenth century.

Rodents and insects are difficult enough to capture let alone stand trial and they underwent a different procedure. They were not judged by civilian courts but by ecclesiastical tribunals based, it seems, on the principle that a curse has a wider radius of action than civil law can cope with. After several examples from a species were seized, tried and condemned, a curse was cast on the whole species.

It was through one such trial that the great French jurist, Bartholomée Chassénée became famous. Assigned to defend mice who had allegedly destroyed a harvest, he began by demanding that all the mice in the diocese should appear at the trial, as he did not know which were the guilty ones. As they quite obviously did not appear, the lawyer then maintained they would not come out of their holes because they were frightened of the prosecutor's cats. So the lawyer laid down that the individuals appearing at the trial should be protected during their coming and going to the tribunal and that if the accused were attacked en route, the opponents would have to pay a large sum of money. When the prosecutors refused to do this, the law suit was placed in the archives and the mice were saved.

Another lawyer established a very interesting ruling. He said the accused should be judged by a jury of individuals of the same species. As the accused in this instance was a bear, no jury could be found.

Nearly every species of animal appeared in front of medieval tribunals but the most badly treated were always black – Satan's favourite colour. Although the Middle Ages and even the terrible Counter-Reformation are now a long way away, no reasonable explanation for such trials has ever been found.

Having witnessed the horrendous treatment poured on animals in the past we should rightly pause to consider the honours that were bestowed upon to counter-balance the wrongs.

We have spoken enough about sacred, untouchable animals but there are some who were not only sacred but also worshipped as gods. The animal cult in Egypt deified animals like the famous oxen Aphis and Memphis, Mnevis at Heliopolis, the ram of Ammon at Thebes, the cat of the goddess Baset at Bubastis and many others, which although not strictly always in animal form were at least, however strange, part human and part animal hybrid. As there was a god of oxen, all oxen were naturally considered sacred and were respected. When they died they were embalmed and buried like the upper classes.

The Greeks also had a cult of animals, but it was more a matter of gods transforming into animals, for reasons of amorous strategy. The most famous example of this is Demetra who was turned into a horse in order to flee the amorous persecutions of Poseidon. It was not uncommon for a cult of animal gods to be practiced for no particular reason such as the god of Aesclepius who was worshipped at Epidaurus in the form of a snake, living underground, or Dionysus who had a temple erected for him with his image graven in the form of a bull.

The bull has always been one of the most worshipped of animals, venerated by all heathen people as a sign of fertility and life. But this honour has made it the most sacrificed of animals because if its blood is spilt in a temple's surroundings, the earth becomes fertile and productive.

On the question of bulls and oxen, a very strange sacrifice was practised by the Romans at Actium on an animal which had nothing sacred about it: the fly. However, sacrificing oxen to the domestic fly was an extremely important event and the Assyrians too had sacrificial rites for flies. Probably these two people were plagued by flies in the summer and sought propitiatory means to keep them away.

We can still see the importance animal myths had and still have in relation to illnesses. The two-tailed lizard is considered in many places to be a powerful talisman against illness. Perhaps the two tails represent an excess of health, or the facility to easily substitute one part of the sick body. However, beware of keeping a green lizard or a snake shut away, you will die of starvation; a toad that is angry can make boils appear on your face and if you jeer at a cuckoo when it is singing your body will become covered with shingles. If by chance a hen should imitate a cock's crow, it means it is bewitched and it is dangerous to eat its eggs. White snakes are raised in the home because it is said they embody the fates and therefore protect the family that gives them hospitality. This is perhaps the one positive superstition amid the horrors in which tradition is so rich.

In Bengal people who wound stag-beetles will find horns growing out of their heads. Whether these are real or metaphorical horns we do not know. In Scotland, it is very unlucky to kill a wren or destroy its nest. In fact, the wren is considered the king of birds in Scotland. Throughout the entire Mediterranean region, the belief is still prevalent that it is dangerous to kill cats and dogs, but in spite of this, they are not treated with care or respect. In Sardinia (this applies only to the health of sheep rather than of men) it is still dangerous for a shepherd to say 'wolf' out loud because a wolf will immediately appear and devour his flock.

All these modern superstitions can be found today in any small, remote village; but in the olden days, they assumed more important forms and were decidedly more religious. For a while there was a 'bond' with dangerous animals which consisted of feigned marriages between a human individual and an animal, usually wolves, foxes, weasels or even dogs, which was supposed to bind the animal with sacred chains and prevent him from harming his human spouse, his family or animals.

At one time, animals were used as a means of chasing away infectious illnesses. When the plague was raging, Arabs would lead a camel round and round the village so it would collect all the illnesses upon itself and then the camel would be strangled – a custom which clearly derives from the Greeks and Romans who used to sacrifice an expiatory goat. This tradition has partially survived in Sardinia although slightly differently. There, an animal who has died from an infectious disease is shot and during epidemics the first animal which appears is shot with a gun. Clearly they are attempting to get rid of the illness through a representative of its carrier. Even more widespread is the case of the transfer of an illness from man to an animal. In the Molise region of Italy, for example, a fat toad was placed under a stone and a magic formula recited which was supposed to make the illness pass from the body of the man to the toad. Another very common usage in many parts of Italy is that of curing mouth ulcers in suckling babes by putting a frog's head in their mouth. In the fifteenth century in Germany, it was believed that to cure petecchial typhus you had to tie a goat to the bed of the sick person: its pungent odour would certainly have overcome the spirit of any illness. Another widespread belief in the Middle Ages was that the best remedy for a scorpion's sting was to travel on the back of a donkey, sitting the wrong way round. In this way, the beast was supposed to absord all the illness.

Chinese medicine has always used animals in a pharmacological context mixed with some magic. The most 'quoted' animals in this field in ancient Chinese medical and pharmacological books are several birds – peacocks, pheasants, kingfishers, cranes and birds of paradise – which are all dressed and treated in special ways and are supposed to cure many illnesses. Bees, too, were considered very useful by the Chinese in pharmacology and in cosmetics. Even today, we hear more than ever about the rediscovery of the famous royal jelly produced by bees.

The only mammal considered at all worthy by the Chinese is the notoriously un-Chinese lion which is imported from India and Africa and is considered to be of divine origin. The lion does not cure illnesses but scares away demon spirits, which seems to be far more an African belief than a Chinese one.

I would like to end this chapter with one superstition which to me is the strangest. In the seventeenth century, scientists decreed that certain ducks were not born from eggs but grew like fruit on the branches of trees. In fact there is even an illustration in the *Historia Naturalis* of Ulysses Aldorvandi, a great naturalist of his time, in which a tree is depicted with branches jutting out over the water. From the branches, strange, fruit-like shapes are hanging which, on ripening, fall into the water and immediately turn into ducklings.

And one last piece of advice proffered by popular wisdom in every country: if you hear a cuckoo singing, listen carefully. For a farmer the number of cuckoo calls indicates how large his crop will be, for old men, it means the number of years they have left to live and for girls the number of years they must wait before they get married.

FEROCITY
OR STARVATION?

Gérard de Nerval and Lobster.

CHAPTER 2

Ferocity or Starvation?

A topic close to superstition is that of ferocity. The myth of ferocity in certain animals has become a legend and is difficult to dispel, in spite of several examples which should be able to destroy these myths.

If, as nearly all naturalists believe, no animal is instinctively afraid of man, it is also true that no animal instinctively hates man, because it is fear which generates hate. Given these premises, it appears that all animals which are considered ferocious, can learn not only not to harm man but also to love him and to become friends with him, like cats and dogs. Some animals one would never suspect of being able to be tamed, can be domesticated after a long and peaceful sojourn with man, once they realize they can trust him and approach him without danger.

For example, who would ever consider taming an African wild boar? It is ugly, awkward and fierce but Dr Schweitzer did and adopted a wild female boar called Josephine. He did nothing towards taming her except to show her some affection and sympathy which she was not accustomed to. Josephine soon grew tame with this treatment and when the mass bells rang out she trotted off to Lambarene with Schweitzer every Sunday and would stay in the chapel with him until the end of the sermon.

Fish are generally considered unfriendly and uncommunicative towards man, but this must be repudiated. In New Zealand, eels come to the banks of the river Anatoki, and take food from a spoon. It has not yet been proved whether eels need a spoon because they are good-mannered or because they fear direct contact with man. Perhaps it is men who fear direct contact with eels.

One of the strangest examples of wild animals being tamed after daily contact with man is the pet lobster which belongs to the French poet, Gérard de Nerval who managed to tame one and even take it for short walks on a lead.

In a large aquarium in London, there is a man whose daily job is to clean the teeth of a baby shark, which has now become quite accustomed to it, and will wait patiently and tolerantly with its mouth wide open.

Particularly interesting is the relationship between man and animals which do not usually interest anybody from a psychological point of view because they are so ugly and have such unsympathetic characters. A crocodile named Mamada grew tame of its own accord, because no one else would have thought of taming him, and lives near the Vai tribe in Liberia where he has elected himself guardian of the village. He keeps away all the fierce crocodiles in the neighbourhood while remaining completely gentle with the villagers. One of the most singular things about this is that his post as guardian must be hereditary since his father and his grandfather did the same thing.

With birds of prey, there is not only the falcon which, as we already know, can easily be adapted for hunting, but also a type of red-necked vulture which answers its master's call and will follow him walking along behind like a dog.

A few years ago, I was staying in a hotel in a small mountain village. One evening a grasshopper jumped through my open window and began to look all around it, curiously unfrightened. It was still there in the morning and when I set out for a walk to the river, I noticed it hopping along beside me. It fell into the habit of following

me every day and I never tried to pick it up or put it in a
box. I christened it Tarantella and it stayed close beside me
like a tiny dog, the whole of my visit. I could have put it in
a box and taken it back to Turin with me but it would have
been like killing it, and so I left it behind to continue its
riverside walks without me.

Where is the border line between ferocity and pure
cruelty? Alan Devoe, an English naturalist, claims that the
most ferocious animal on earth is the shrew, a tiny animal
that many people have seen probably without recognising
it, because it is so common. In an article supporting his
theory, Alan Devoe illustrated the bloodthirsty activities of
this minuscule animal.

The shrew, he says, is so bloodthirsty that it attacks, kills
and devours animals twice its own size. It has such a
prodigious appetite that it eats considerably more than its
own weight every day, and burns energy so fast that when it
is deprived of its food supply, it dies of starvation in less
than a day. The shrew knows no fear. One day when he was
a boy, Devoe put a shrew into a cage with a young white
mouse, intending to leave it there for a few minutes while he
prepared a cage for the shrew. But straightaway the velvety
morsel was on its hind legs, had bared its teeth and let out a
shrill scream, grinding its teeth in rage and hunger. Terrified, his timid adversary huddled in one corner, and then
with a flash the shrew was on his back, tearing his throat
to pieces and attacking him all over. In the end, the shrew
swallowed the mouse right down to the very last scrap,
including bones, claws and skin.

There is an idyllic period during a shrew's life when both
father and mother live happily together. But this is the only
period when their ferocity is abated. To put two shrews
together in the same cage is fatal because after a few
minutes only one is left, licking its chops.

On this evidence, should we think of the shrew as a fierce
animal? Is a creature fierce when it must eat the equivalent

of its own weight every three hours, if it is not to die of starvation? Is it its fault if its physical structure compels it to attack and procure food if it is not to die? The shrew is tiny and on average weights 14 grammes. Its aggression is a direct consequence of the absurd connection between its need for food and its size.

There are not many cruel animals but some of the most graceful are among those that are cruel. The roebuck with its seemingly soft and timid nature is not only ferocious and cruel but vile too. It treacherously attacks animals weaker than itself, even those of the same species and quite often will attack its own partner and offspring.

The agreeable turtle dove becomes a sadist when imprisoned. If a female turtle dove is left in a cage with a male when she is not in the mating season, she will attack him with her beak and, without actually killing him, will leave him half dead.

Without a doubt the cruellest animal of all is the shrike or butcher-bird. This beautiful, peaceful-looking bird, which feeds on all the small animals it can find, is hardly ever hungry, but amuses itself by killing and does this in the most unpleasant way. Having captured its prey, it pierces it alive on a thorn or a sharp twig, and leaves it there to die without ever coming back to eat it. It is almost as if it were a game. Perhaps it is a reaffirmation of its ability to hunt.

Another ferocious animal is the river otter which is persecuted by hunters, not only for its valuable skin, but also to preserve the fishing grounds where it lives. An adult otter, without even being hungry, can kill up to 100 kilogrammes of fish in one single night through pure cruelty.

Then there is the 'stumpy-tail', a completely innocuous-looking reptile from Australia which is harmless towards man but not towards snakes for which it harbours a personal hatred since it attacks them all indiscriminately, even those which are much larger than itself, and always manages to kill them. For this reason it is tamed and kept in Australian homes as an extra valuable guard dog.

Animals which are halfway between ferocity and cruelty are African wild dogs and hyenas, which specialise in psychological hunting – the cruellest method that exists because the prey gives up more through fear than lack of strength. The African wild dog which resembles the wolf, lives south of the Sahara, and attacks animals larger than itself like oxen and horses, terrifying them by howling fiercely. Being an extremely fast runner, it will then follow them until the prey, exhausted and terrified, collapses and is immediately gored in the stomach by the wild dog's tusks. The hyena, notorious for feeding off crows, also has an astute psychological method of attack. When it senses a lion is close to death, the hyena attaches itself to it, following like a shadow but never attacking. The lion in all probability knows where his mortal remains will finish up and becomes furious when he sees the hyena, but weakened through old age or illness, he is forced to endure this silent presence which certainly does not help prolong his life.

In the world of marine animals, the fiercest predator is not the shark, as most people believe, which will generally attack only where there is blood, or the piranha or the barracuda. The terror of the seas is the ork, or killer whale, which belongs to the delightful dolphin family, from whom it seems to have inherited very little. The ork grows to a length of 10 metres and attacks every animal it meets in the water, killing marine birds, seals and penguins, and sometimes even attacking large boats. At times, its thirst for blood will take it inshore to ports where it devours whales which have been dragged in by the whaling boats.

In the ork's world, as in man's, absolute dimensions of good and evil are blurred, but there is a story which illustrates how this terror of the high seas, can be tamed, can be made to eat out of your hand and show affection to those feeding it.

In 1964, Samuel Burish, the sculptor, was commissioned to kill an ork and make a model of it for the Vancouver Aquarium. It was not an easy task, because orks are as intelligent as dolphins but less friendly and, if wounded, can become very dangerous.

On July 16, 1964, Burish managed to harpoon an ork and set out to kill it. When he took aim, the ork fixed him in the eye with such a stare that he was unable to become its executioner. He immediately contacted Vancouver Zoo over the radio in an attempt to save the ork. The zoo officials went wild with excitement because only one ork had ever been captured before, and it had died 18 hours afterwards. This ork was as docile as a puppy and allowed itself to be attached to a 180-metre leash and towed back to Vancouver.

On the ork's arrival, the director of the shipyard generously offered a dry dock, and an entire sanitary squad including all branches of medicines was there to attend the ork.

Its first friend was the very man who had tried to kill it. Every morning Burich, maintaining the ork needed company, would visit it in a small dinghy which the ork, by now named Moby, could have easily shattered with the flip of a fin. The wound had healed but Moby still refused food. The situation was becoming serious despite daily vitamin injections to stimulate his appetite. After 55 days without food, Moby was finally convinced that no one wanted to poison him and began eating 50 kilogrammes of fish a day and gradually became more sociable and playful. One day he was offered a sea scorpion but refused it slapping his tail in annoyance. When the sea scorpion was offered to him a second time with its sharp fins removed, he gratefully accepted it. He evidently had very defined and delicate tastes. Many experiments were done on Moby and when he listened to a recording of other orks he squeaked with excitement, but remained completely indifferent when he heard his own voice.

Moby also learned to roll over on his back and have his tummy tickled. When he died, the *Times* published a two-column obituary – the same space that was dedicated to the announcement of the outbreak of World War II.

Another story is that of the stone bass, Ulysses, told by Jacques Cousteau and James Dugan in their book *Life in the Sea* which took place in the Indian Ocean near Assumption where it seemed, no one had ever been before. The fish were so fearless that they came close to the ciné cameras in curiosity and explored the strange animals with their machines and equipment. The fish were infinite in number including species never before seen or imagined. All were friendly and completely without fear of man. Cousteau's sojourn in these waters was prolonged for some time, one of the main reasons being Ulysses.

They stayed there for 40 days, none of them losing their enthusiasm for the Assumption reef. One of the reasons was the extraordinary fish Luis Marden met: a 27-kg stone bass or 'grouper' with brown skin whose pale marbled effect changed every so often. The large fish approached Marden as he was preparing to photograph it. It touched the lighting man with its nose. Marden withdrew to get the fish in a better light and after a series of many such withdrawals finally took a photograph at the right distance and then dived off deeper in search of other subjects. But the stone bass came up behind him and nuzzled him and his camera. When Marden tried to take a photograph of another fish, the large stone bass placed itself between Marden and the object.

When Marden told the rest of the crew about his new acquaintance they all dived down carrying a bag full of meat with them. The big fish swam towards the divers without hesitation. They dropped several pieces of meat into the water – the stone bass opened its cavernous mouth and the pieces of meat disappeared inside like a flock of birds flying into a tunnel. When they cautiously tried feeding it by hand, the big fish, took the pieces from the tips of their fingers without hurting them. It was christened Ulysees.

It became an inseperable friend for Cousteau and his crew. It followed them everywhere sometimes rubbing itself against their rubber flippers. In a short time Ulysses learned their diving time-table and the following morning was found waiting for them to make their first dive of the day.

If he was in a good mood, Ulysses would allow himself to be caressed and have his head scratched by one of the divers. Once Dalmas, another of the crew members, hid the sack of meat and began gyrating slowly around, as if he were dancing in the water. Following the bait, Ulysses did the same. Then Dalmas swivelled round the other way and Ulysses again copied him. Their movements were so agile and rhythmical that the others managed to film them and said they looked like two ballerinas doing a graceful waltz. One morning when Dalmas opened the cloth bag to give Ulysses a piece of meat, the big fish snatched the bag rapidly from Dalmas' hands and swallowed it whole.

The morning after, Ulysses was not under the step. In the afternoon, the divers spread out to search for him. He was found lying on the sand in front of his den, a large crevice in the coral reef. All that was missing was the name plate above the door. But Ulysses was not interested in the divers that day. The morning after he was still 'in bed' and the third day he was stretched out on one side looking very ill. The ship's doctor, Denis Martin-Laval, was consulted and he diagnosed a serious and possibly fatal intestinal obstruction. Martin-Lavel found himself faced with the most unusual case of his whole career. As he could not bring the patient into the operating theatre, he had to visit the fish at his own bedside. The doctor took anaesthetics, haemostatic forceps, needles and gut with him which he used to suture the incision after he had extracted the cloth bag from inside the suffering Ulysses.

At first light the next day, a patrol dived down and found that Ulysses had disappeared from his veranda. Some divers went off to look for him, when one felt the oxygen cylinder on his back being tugged. It was Ulysses announcing he was better. He appeared happy and hungry now that he had got rid of his cloth bag.

Following this expedition, Ulysses was heard of again from a boat on a round-the-world trip which purposely put into port at Assumption and sent some divers down to look for Ulysses. They immediately recognised him and he swam round the divers, appearing happy and in good health.

This is what I mean by 'magic': the transformation of valuable food into a dear, everyday friend for whose health one risks one's own life to do a very difficult underwater operation, in the most uncomfortable conditions one can imagine, and then, at the end, release the fish for its own good.

It seems that subsequent divers tried to feed the other fish, but there were tremendous scenes of jealousy from Ulysses, but in my opinion, these were from sentimental rather than self interested reasons.

Ulysses knew quite well that his human friends would continue to feed him every day in spite of the fact that he was perfectly capable of feeding himself, but he did not want them to transfer their attentions to the other fish. It is pleasing to think that every so often, men are capable of considering a fish not just as a tasty dish or a laboratory guinea pig.

INTELLIGENCE

Chumley the Chimp

CHAPTER 3

Intelligence

Ever since Aristotle's time, biologists the world over have continued to be passionately involved in research on animal intelligence and experiments daily furnish them with more interesting results. Are animals gifted with intelligence or not? It is now a long time since the great Déscartes asserted that animals acted involuntarily, which proves that he could never have known any, or that his brain was so constituted that it is difficult, with every respect, to imagine how he ever came to write *Discourse on Method* or *Meditations*.

Experiments in scientific laboratories irrefutably show that when an animal's brain is given instruction it develops far more quickly than other brains, and that as the brain grows the intelligence increases.

The best known experiments are on mice who learn in a short space of time to find their way out of labyrinths in which painful stimuli have been placed along the route with a succulent piece of cheese at the exit.

The most interesting mouse experiment took place in an American laboratory but it can also be done in any home without too much difficulty. A food distributor, based on a very simple principle, was placed in a cage. Every few minutes the mouse pressed down a lever and a piece of food came out of an opening. When several mice had been taught to do this, conditions were slightly altered. The mice were all put in the same cage where the lever is situated at the opposite end from the opening where the food came out. The mice understood the change and a tense situation immediately developed.

If there were three mice, the one that worked the lever will never get a single piece of food because the others have all had time to grab it from the other side of the cage. On the first day of the American experiment, not one of the mice touched the lever and the three mice mounted relentless guard over the distributor, from which, obviously, no particles of food appeared. The second day, one of the mice worked the lever but to the sole advantage of his two companions. On the fourth day one of the mice was struck by a ray of genius. He pressed the lever rapidly three times, letting his companions take their piece of food and then ate his own in complete tranquillity. Then he returned to work and in less than 2 hours had made 1,156 pieces of food appear from the distributor.

But there are intelligent mice, lazy mice and cunning mice. It has been shown that intelligence is hereditary. The offspring of two intelligent mice are more intelligent than the offspring of two stupid mice. Experiments on mice are infinite, interesting and sometimes amusing, although they can also, at times, be cruel. Mice are the preferred laboratory animals because they are small, cheap and reproduce very easily.

In Innsbruck in 1880, a woman was accused by her employer of stealing eggs from the hen coop. She swore, in her own defence, that mice were stealing the eggs. Even if this appears absurd and you cannot imagine a mouse carrying an egg in its arms, the judge ordered an experiment to be carried out in the courtroom. Two mice and an egg were brought in and the mice set free. After a few minutes of uncertainty, one of the mice got hold of the egg with its front legs while the other took the other end in its teeth and together they dragged the egg into a corner where they peacefully ate the fruit of their toil.

Everyone knows parrots can learn to talk and the ancient Romans knew this as well, and were perhaps their first masters. To train them, they placed the parrot in front of a mirror and themselves behind and continued to repeat the same phrases over and over until the parrot believing that its reflection was a rival, was forced to imitate the words. In the late empire, parrots were so expensive that they cost more to keep than slaves. They were not wrongly valued, seeing that in 885 the life of Emperor Basil's son, Leone, was saved by a parrot. Basil was the emperor of Byzantium and had condemned his son to death, but revoked the order when Leone's parrot began to chant "Poor Leone, Poor Leone".

Many scientists believe talking birds just repeat the sounds they hear without understanding what the words mean. It could be that this is how it is with some birds, but it is certainly not a hard and fast rule for all of them. The following episode will confirm it. I want to tell it because I am certain of its authenticity since it happened in my family and shows not only the capacity certain talking animals have for reason but also their other qualities and weaknesses, like affection for their master and consequent jealousy on their behalf.

This is the story. Many years ago, my grandmother had a parrot called Polly, as nearly every parrot in the world is named. It adored my grandmother and made her speeches which were perfectly to the point although not very complicated in their vocabularly. It said "good morning", enquired after her health and often repeated its favourite phrase "How is life with you, mistress?". Polly lived a happy and undisturbed life at home until my grandmother, who absolutely adored animals, had the unhappy idea of acquiring a marmot called Ghita (perhaps not everybody knows this, since marmots are less well known than parrots, but once upon a time all domesticated marmots were called Ghita). Naturally, the new animal excited the interest of the entire family, and took up a lot of our attention, although Polly continued to be just as much loved and admired as before. But this was not enough for it. It began repeating with an increasingly sadder air "Poor Polly, Mistress loves Ghita better and doesn't love poor Polly any more". In spite of all our assurances which we continually repeated about our unchanged affection, Polly could not bear the thought that the affection which had formerly been its alone, now had to be shared with another; it began to waste away and after a short while it died. The strange thing is that it never hated Ghita, the object of its jealousy: it just suffered and died. Animals are better than men at this but we will talk of this later, when we examine the affectionate relationships between animals. Here, I just wanted to give an example of how certain talking birds know what they are saying.

The pigeon is misunderstood because it is so common, but it can easily be tamed and becomes attached to its owner. Its exceptional sense of direction helps it to undertake duties which could be defined as the emotional bonds we generally think of in the context of cats and dogs. The homing pigeon returns home as a normal event and it is almost its profession, but a pigeon which traces an unknown place for a reunion with somebody it loves, is completely different.

This happened some years ago in England where a boy had tamed a pigeon and both were very fond of each other. The boy had to go to a hospital for an operation far from home, and one evening as he lay sad and alone in his hospital ward, he heard a tapping at the window. He asked the nurse to open the window and his absurd hope was then realised. Guided by affection and goodness knows what else, his pigeon had found him.

Pigeons are very sympathetic animals and should be

more appreciated and less eaten, because they often do comical and intelligent things. A couple of London pigeons became famous because they regularly took the Underground to cross London and probably knew the most interesting stations from a gastronomic or touristic point of view.

But the most curious episode happened several years ago at Borlänge in Sweden where a woman fed a pigeon every day. One day the pigeon, which had obviously decided to move on, appeared carrying a banknote worth five crowns in its beak: it deposited it in the woman's hand, flew off and was never seen again. Naturally, many explanations were offered but the most positive reason seems to be the least probable to me, that the pigeon was killed by the person from whom it had stolen the money. The idea of a gift is often quite clear in the minds of animals, contrary to what most people believe, and there is also the rather absurd reason that it was payment for its food. But my explanation is this: this intelligent bird, knowing it was going to depart for another place, decided to pay homage to its benefactress and having noticed that these strange pieces of money seemed to be valued among men, it got hold of one and brought it to the woman. Naturally, the pigeon could have worked out that the value of the food it had received was exactly five crowns but this seems to me to be rather too far-fetched even for a pigeon Einstein.

Also our small common sparrow is anything but stupid. It knows which houses give it food to eat and there is one which comes on to my balcony every day, protesting energetically if I do not give it enough bread crusts and shrieks noisily until it gets what it wants. But sparrows are not only lively animals individually. When, for example, they fly in formation and meet a net in their flight path, they never dream of flying up over the net, which would retard them on their journey (who knows what urgent things they have to do) but they fold their wings against them close to their bodies so that they can pass through the holes.

Many birds love objects which glitter and an aviary-keeper in Southampton has profited from this weakness and animal intelligence. He has taught two magpies and two crows to take the small coins offered by visitors in their beaks. The four birds learned this immediately and, given the English passion for animals, earn a tidy sum each day.

The albatross is another bird which should be taken into consideration. When he was young the German Count von Luckener went to sea as a cabin boy aboard the Russian ship, *Niobe*. One evening far from land, he fell into the sea and would certainly have drowned if an enormous albatross had not come to his rescue, grasped him between his wings and kept him afloat until the sailors on the ship could reach him and pull him to safety. One asks if the albatross would have acted in the same way towards an adult or whether this was a case of that strange affinity and protective sense that animals are said to feel when confronted by the young of any species, including humans.

Intelligent animals can be divided into three categories; the greatest number use their intelligence in a primarily utilitarian way, those who use it in an altruistic way and the rarest group – those who use it in a theoretical way. Sparrows belong to the first group which I spoke of before and also all the animals which use their intelligence to overcome obstacles or to obtain something they want, like the mice. This type of intelligence is the one that is nearest instinct, from which it is decidedly difficult to distinguish at times. The bird which makes its nest in a certain way or the mother which protects her young by hiding them is using her intelligence in an instinctive way and certain relentless materialists refuse to define this faculty as intelligence at all.

An episode which illustrates a strictly utilitarian but certainly never instinctive intelligence, happened some years ago in Texas where a mule gave an excellent display of its intellectual capacity. It loved the fruit of the Japanese persimmon tree but naturally never managed to get at it because it could not climb trees. Then it had the brilliant idea of placing its hind legs against the desired tree and shaking it with powerful kicks, easily managing to make the ripe fruit fall down. Seeing this method worked, it used it every time it came across these trees.

The harvest crab is far-sighted, as well as being intelligent, and cuts seaweed with its pincers, rolling it into large leaves and making packages which it carries back to its refuge to keep for a rainy day.

Ants should also be mentioned in the context of far-sightedness. Their social structure is well known and the Eciton species of ants from Guiana unite in their thousands to form an ant bridge to the ground when they are up trees and do not want all the trouble of journeying down the tree.

Baker ants grind grains of rice down until they are reduced to a pulp which they then roll out into small round cakes, which they leave to cook in the sun for several hours. If this is not 'magic' . . .

The smallest insects can often beat superior animals in utilitarian intelligence. There is a type of wasp, the digger wasp (*ammophila minaria*) which, to close the entrance to its nest, presses earth, beating it with a fragment of stone which it uses as a hammer.

The albatross and the seal belong to the second group using altruism. A seal once saved a young girl who was drowning and her companion who was trying to go for help, by keeping them both afloat with its large caudal fin. There was the sailor who fell overboard in the Pacific and would have drowned if a sea-turtle which he was gripping on to, had not been aware that the sailor's life depended exclusively on it and went for over 15 hours without diving.

Animals which are gifted with theoretical intelligence are the most well-known ones who can read, write and count. Let us look instead at examples in which animals, not particularly noted for their intelligence, have astounded scientists and others. One would rarely think of calling an octopus 'intelligent'. One generally looks at its strange physical qualities and its method of hunting and self defence. But the octopus is an invertebrate with a large brain and is therefore more intelligent. This allows it to be tamed and also to do some constructive reasoning on its own. It learns with ease to eat from the hand which offers it food, and even to pull at the fingers to open the hand which is hiding food. In Brighton, a story is still told of an octopus which used to get out of its tank at night, follow the wall round until it arrived at another tank containing fish, have a snack and return home. In Florida, a zoologist has taught an octopus to remove the lid from a glass container and take out the crabs.

Alan Devoe wrote that he once asked a famous zoologist what was the most remarkable action he had seen a wild animal perform. After some thought about large, cour-ageous animals such as wolves and raccoons, the zoologist smiled and said the most extraordinary animal was an insect.

One day, he was on the bank of a stream when he noticed a scavenger wasp on the ground beside him. This wasp had paralysed a large spider and was attempting in vain to drag it to its lair. But it could not manage to take off with such a heavy load and carrying it across the ground was proving too difficult. Finally, the wasp dragged the spider to the nearby stream and put it in the water. Keeping hold of the body which was now floating on the surface, the wasp began to flap its wings as fast as it could. Slowly, like a helicopter hauling a barge, the wasp towed the spider for about 80 yards downstream while the fascinated zoologist followed on ground. Suddenly, the wasp turned towards the bank and a moment later pulled its dripping treasure on to the shore. There, a few inches from the water was its lair. Exhausted but triumphant the insect dragged the trophy it had acquired with such difficulty to its nest.

In that unforgettable glance he gave the world of insects,

the zoologist said later, he understood that they too had their Galileos and their Christopher Columbuses.

When animals are attracted by food or find themselves in danger, they reveal an incredible ingenuity. A man once put a bird-table in his garden to attract the birds but found that it was always emptied by the squirrels who got a good bellyful before even one bird could get near. Then the man bought a special bird table. It had a circular tray, balanced in such a way that if anything heavier than a small bird alighted on it, it overturned and the intruder crashed to the ground, but not the feeding tray which was placed in a central compartment. For several days the squirrels, one by one, jumped on to the tray and fell off without being able to touch the feed. A few days later, however, the man realised the bird table began to empty again as fast as before and he hid to spy on the table. What he saw could not help but strike and fill him with admiration for the intelligence of the squirrels. Two of them, when they were sure not to be seen, climbed up on a branch, took steady aim and jumped together on either side of the circular tray and thus tranquilly breakfasted. I do not know whether the man still had the courage to find new ways of chasing away these astute animals; they certainly merited the food they managed to take. The most interesting thing about this episode is that the squirrels, besides understanding the principle of equilibrium perfectly had evidently consulted together and devised this brilliant plan.

Another entertaining episode happened several years ago when a woman and her husband were driving slowly along a coast road in Cornwall to admire the splendid view. They had plenty of time to notice a low-flying seagull which had heard the car and dropped a small pile of molluscs right in front of it. This was not a homage to the traveller but a clever plan to secure his breakfast. When the seagull saw that the car had not driven over his molluscs which were slightly to the left, he let out a clear scream of protest.

Realising his intentions and amused at the shameless effrontery of the gull, the driver reversed so they would drive over
the molluscs and smash the shells. When they looked
round, the seagull was blissfully eating his molluscs which
had been perfectly shelled.

A beaver hunter once witnessed a scene and was so
struck by the intelligence of the protagonist that it per-
suaded him to save the lives of a whole group of beavers.
The traditional way to catch beavers is to spring a 1-foot
leak in their dam and place traps in the hole. As the level of
the water falls, the beavers hasten to repair the damage and
fall into the trap.

This particular hunter was in Canada with a friend and
found the day after that the leak in the dam had been
mended and the traps buried in the sand. This went on for
several days until one evening the two men hid on the river
bank to watch. When it became dark, a beaver came out of
his lair to inspect the leak and then swam off up river. After
a while he returned pulling a piece of wood behind him
which he pushed into the trap to make it spring shut. Then
he disappeared again, returning later with two beavers, and
together they mended the hole. From that evening on the
two hunters left the beavers in peace. It is miraculous that
the beavers recognised there was a trap without first falling
into it.

Another animal which knows how to deal with traps
when it is caught in them is the leopard. This splendid
animal can leap 14 yards, hides where a tiger would not
even venture, is perfectly camouflaged and has such acute
hearing that it can spot the smallest sound and the direction
it is coming from. The leopard trusts almost entirely in its
high intelligence. Generally speaking it is not a man-eater,
but if it samples man once, it realises how easy it is and tries
again. Man's traps give it little trouble. It is the only animal
which, when it has fallen into a trap, realises that crying out
will only attract the hunter's attention. So, as soon as it gets

caught, it silently begins to free itself and succeeds in most cases, thanks to its intelligence and its prodigious strength. A leopard was once seen freeing itself by placing its free paw in the jaws of the iron trap and bending it back.

As well as being intelligent this formidable hunter is also astute. A hunter once saw a leopard in Kenya misleading the buffalo it was chasing by masking its own smell and rolling in buffalo excrement. Conjugally, leopards are very happy and often hunt in pairs, perfectly planning each task down to the last second.

Wolves are among the most intelligent and efficient of hunters. Their packs are co-ordinated to the point where each individual knows its duty, executing it perfectly and at the right moment. Wolves communicate well among themselves. They understand the weak points of their prey: in winter, they force deer on to the ice where their hooves cannot get a grip; in summer they force them to swim until they are exhausted and patrol the river bank so there is no means of escape.

The wolf has two weak points only which are naturally exploited by hunters – gluttony and habit. They may be cunning and intelligent but they are fooled by poisoned bait, and they can never relinquish the habit of 'marking' the same place during their walks. This habit, inherited by the dog with less harmful effects, often costs the wolf its life. The hunter identifies the 'marked' place, sets a trap drenched with the smell of another wolf, and the game is over. When the 'landowner' wolf returns and smells the strange scent, it begins to scratch the ground and the trap springs shut on it.

Dolphins

Nearly every scientist is agreed that the dolphin is the most intelligent animal of all. Dolphins are endowed with a brain which is proportionately much larger than man's and should, consequently, be more intelligent than man himself.

Their IQ is certainly very high and experiments are being done which give one great hope for the future. It is only relatively recently that scientists have decided to apply themselves seriously to these gifted animals.

Plutarch wrote 25 centuries ago that the dolphin was the only animal which loved man for himself. Among animals on land, some shun man, while domestic animals like cats and dogs obey man because he gives them food. It is only the dolphin which possesses what all philosophers have been searching for: altruistic friendship.

There are several legends, the most well known being that of Arione who was saved from a storm by a dolphin. Ichthyologists who are sceptical about anthropomorphism have maintained for years that dolphins never had any desire to save lives, but acted in this way simply because it amused them to push objects around, including human objects. Dolphins are, of course, great game lovers and fortunately good-natured, otherwise their terrible teeth, numbering from 160 to 212, would make them as frightening as their cousins, the orks. Although dolphins are happy and playful, their games can sometimes become a bit rough and are not always well received. In Australia, a boat with three fishermen on board was taken over and used as a football by a group of dolphins, who divided into two teams and enjoyed themselves enormously making the boat leap out of the water, to the much lesser amusement of the fishermen.

One of the most well-known episodes about dolphins is the one about Pelorus Jack, certainly the most famous dolphin in history. Pelorus Jack was a dolphin pilot and was spotted for the first time in 1888 in Pelorus Sound in New Zealand where he was found guiding a boat between the rocks of Cook Straits and French Pass, a very dangerous passage which is often fatal for many ships. When the sailors registered the dolphin's ability as a pilot, they began following him as a matter of course and he soon learned to meet every ship entering or leaving the sound. Here, it was certainly not a matter of the dolphin amusing himself by pushing. However, he never guided a sailing ship which leads one to suppose that he did not do it from the goodness of his soul but because he liked the sound of the engines.

In 1962 Professor J. Lilly was subsidised by N.A.S.A. to complete his studies on dolphin language and he discovered that they talked continuously among themselves using an extremely complex language and that they were capable of imitating any sound and of learning the human language. Since the film *The Day of the Dolphin* whose stars are two congenial dolphins learning to talk, such discussions have become fashionable but nothing has yet transpired from the work in Florida. Perhaps the dolphins in the film were exaggerated but one cannot say this with any authority until there is an official pronouncement.

In a few years' time maybe we will have animal interpreters who will keep us in touch with what is happening in the underwater world. But there are many other uses to which dolphins could be put – rapid transport of messages, as underwater workmen, to put cable in place, perhaps even as saboteurs of enemy units. I should add that dolphins are also obliging, doing whatever is asked of them, even though they may not find it amusing. In Japan, for example, dolphins have been trained to push shoals of fish towards fishing nets and often learn to single out the species of fish which the fishermen want.

It would be interesting to see if, once trained perfectly, dolphins developed along with their intelligence a moral sense which would prevent them from carrying out certain orders such as catching fish, sabotaging instruments or plundering sunken ships. In the film I mentioned, the dolphins learnt the difference between good and evil when they had to push a ship out of the water and would do it without hesitation if it was a boat which belonged to the enemy. One cannot help but wonder what would happen if dolphins were taught by man's system of thought, criteria and way of life. There might then be dolphin philosophers, competitive dolphins and even dolphins that were conscientious objectors.

Dolphins can move at a speed of up to 60 kilometres an hour while their normal speed averages at about 30 kilometres an hour, which is quite remarkable when you realise that dolphins stay willingly in muddy estuary waters and hunt in the deep where the light is almost totally reduced.

A collision with a reef at 30 kilometres an hour would be serious for a dolphin but it never runs into this danger. Nature has wisely endowed it with a perfect system for singling out obstacles, similar to man's sonar system, used by ships. But there is a difference: while sonar emissions are at a fixed frequency, the dolphins' are variable as is the intensity of the signals sent out.

Experiments by Kellog in Florida have shown that the dolphins' sonar system is a substitute for his sight, which is useless in muddy or turbulent waters and for his non-existent sense of smell, and also a substitute for taste. Five senses are therefore concentrated into one, but this is not all. The dolphin's sonar has another quality which makes it seem almost magical to those who are not used to seeing it in action. Its sensitivity is so acute that it can receive different echoes from different materials and even from different organisms. Man's sonar system cannot distinguish a wooden ship from a metal one and sometimes even mistakes a whale for a submarine. The dolphin's sonar distinguishes between two fish of the same structure but of different species. Kellog's experiments have shown conclusively that the dolphins can immediately distinguish a fish it prefers from one it does not.

What would happen if, having learned man's techniques and blended then with their own, dolphins decided to rebel against man one day? This science fiction vision is probably far off but since we see science fiction daily becoming science and life, I believe there is a case for giving this possibility serious thought.

Elephants and Dogs

Aristotle crowned the elephant with the wreath of intelligence which is no mean compliment coming from him. The elephant lives about the same number of years as man, reaching his psychic maturity at the same age with more or less the same sexual habits. In spite of this, the elephant has never been appreciated especially in the modern world and its life is at risk from man if man continues carrying it towards extinction. Man has finally become aware of its great intelligence and scientists are now studying it seriously. In Eastern countries, people take notice of the intelligence and docility of animals and profit, by making them work strenuously and sometimes on their own and independently of man.

The elephant is such an intelligent animal that it learns everything it is taught to do instantly and continues daily carrying out tasks assigned to it, without ever making a mistake.

Elephant intelligence is so able that they never stop learning, however much is taught them, and they never forget. Elephants continue to learn all their lives and even learn things no one has taught them but which have come into their minds on their own. Some elephants have learned to stop the clatter of the bell around their necks with mud so that they can creep into banana groves without anybody hearing amd stuff themselves full of bananas. If part of their body itches and they cannot reach it with the trunks, they will get a branch and use it as a backscratcher.

Colonel Williams, nicknamed Elephant Bill, told many tales in a beautiful book of elephant adventures which he witnessed and which convinced him never to shoot an elephant again.

Elephants enjoyed a certain respect in antiquity – certainly, far more than in the modern world – and were honoured with a mention by Plutarch. Plutarch tells of how a large elephant passed by every day in a street frequented by spiteful schoolchildren. One day the beast, vexed by the continual goading and having his trunk pulled so often, lost a little of his boundless patience and lifted up one of the boys in his trunk giving him quite a shock, before placing him back delicately on the ground. He could quite easily have dropped him and crushed him under foot, but he seemed to want to teach him a lesson.

Jean Gaivet tells the story of good-natured cunning in elephants. In an Indian village, an elephant which was carrying timber, passed in front of a tailor's shop every day and was usually offered an apple or a carrot. One day, the tailor played a trick on the elephant so that when he stretched out his trunk to receive the customary gift, he was pricked by a hatpin. The trunk is one of the most sensitive parts of an elephant and the poor beast went off disillusioned and in pain, but without reacting. However, the next time he passed the tailor's shop, he filled his trunk with water before he got there and sprayed his old friend with such force that it made any further wish to play practical jokes disappear.

Besides greed and a touch of laziness, elephants have one great vice – they are mad about alcohol. This naturally only applies to tame elephants who have had the opportunity to taste it, but some elephants have even discovered how to distill alcohol. Elephants use their cunning too to procure what they want. A keeper once gave two chilled elephants some whisky and from that day on, whenever he appeared the two elephants inexplicably began to sneeze and shiver.

Since elephants are also rather lazy, their cunning aids them in finding excuses for not working. An old female elephant, Ruth who had hurt her leg, continued pretending it still hurt her and wailing whenever anyone approached her for some time after it was perfectly healed. The trick continued until the keeper saw, when she was not aware of it, that she could play, walk and trot quite well and that her leg was perfectly all right. He severely reprimanded her and told her the game was over. Ruth understood and went back to work.

Bill Ryan, a hunter in Nairobi tells how once, in a permanent encampment, a herd of elephants was in the habit of going into an orchard and stripping the trees of their fruit and green leaves. The hunters set up a new enclosure which the elephants immediately broke through. Another new enclosure was built and attached to an electric current. After a while the elephants deduced that when all the lights went out in the camp there was no longer any electric current in the fence. One particularly bright elephant discovered that ivory did not conduct electricity. Defeated, the hunters took up their former methods of armed guard.

Elephants also possess a distinct sense of humour and each one of them has a different character and enjoys playing jokes. In Kenya, for example, there was a famous elephant who amused himself by frightening tourists without doing them any harm. He used to position himself in the road behind a bend and wait for cars. When one arrived, he would walk out from his hiding place, his enormous ears flapping in the wind and trumpeting ferociously. When the occupants of the car looked terrified enough, he would turn around and let them pass, looking after them with such an amused look, one could almost say he was grinning maliciously.

Elephants have a surprising capacity for kindness and affection. Keepers in the National Parks of Kenya and Tanzania tell numerous tales about this and the great sense of solidarity that unites them. If an elephant is wounded, the others will come to its side, place their tusks under his and carry him out of danger, sometimes journeying like this for miles. This solidarity goes to the extremes of vendettas especially when females and young ones are involved. If a hunter kills a female elephant, the whole herd will band together to see that justice is done – and a charging herd of furious elephants is one of the most terrifying spectacles imaginable. If the hunters manage to run to safety, a small group of 'doctor' elephants will check to see whether the female is still alive and will try and bring her back to life by standing her on her feet and hitting her with their trunks. When they are sure she is dead, they return to the forest leading the orphaned elephant with them.

Just as they are tender mothers, female elephants are also tender lovers and are the most similar to man in this field. Courting starts long before the female goes on heat. There is a flirting session with kisses and caresses similar to human kisses, and offers of fresh grass which correspond to our bunch of flowers. The two lovers never separate and continue exchanging caresses right until the moment of mating which always takes place in remote spots. There is then a honeymoon which lasts about 10 months. The couple remain aloof from the rest of the herd and continue their amorous games by night. From the moment she is pregnant the female elephant loses all interest in her partner, transferring it to her unborn child.

During the 21-month gestation period, the future mother hangs around with an older midwife elephant who protects her from dangers and helps her during childbirth. The maternal instinct in the female has a corresponding instinct in the male which shows strong protective feelings towards both small and old elephants.

Elephants have an excellent memory for kindnesses shown to them. Once a planter in Kenya captured a small elephant who had a nasty wound on his foot. He treated it, making him suffer a bit, but the wound healed. Some time later, the planter came across the elephant again and his hand was taken in the elephant's trunk and placed on the old wound.

Among elephant keepers, the story of Black Diamond is already a legend. He was a circus elephant who adored his keeper and was so jealous he could not endure the keeper's wife who often came to the circus to meet him. If the couple were standing too close together in the elephant's opinion, he would trumpet furiously and create a jealous scene. One day he was sold to another circus and several years later, his original keeper came to seek him out. The elephant gave him a joyous welcome, embracing him with his trunk. A year later, the man went to see him again, this time accompanied by a woman. Perhaps he was showing off how the elephant recognised and welcomed him, but he was to pay for his pride. Black Diamond was taken by a spasm of furious jealousy and attacked the woman and killed her.

The tragic story of Bozo, the circus elephant who was condemned to death, happened some years ago. Bozo was a well educated animal and a favourite with children. In the circus ring, he would waltz, pirouette, and stretch himself out on the ground pretending to be dead. As a grand finale, he would conduct the orchestra with a flag. But one day, he suddenly changed and tried to kill his keeper three times in a week; he brayed furiously at children who offered him nuts as if he wanted to trample them down. Nothing would calm him. The authorities told the proprietor the animal had become a public menace and would have to be put to death.

At that time there were no societies to protect animals or to intervene when the circus owner sold tickets to the public for Bozo's execution. The crowd which filled the circus saw a group of armed soldiers, a platoon of riflemen and Bozo in a large circular cage, turning round and round ceaselessly. Every so often, he lifted up his trunk and brayed as if he knew what fate was awaiting him. Outside the cage, the ringmaster, dressed in tails, stood on an illuminated barrel and was preparing to give the signal to fire when he felt a hand upon his shoulder.

Behind him stood a small, thickset man with brown whiskers, thick glasses and a chestnut-coloured bowler hat.

"Wouldn't you prefer to see this animal live?" asked the unknown person.

"It's impossible," replied the manager, "he has turned rogue and there's no way of curing him now."

"Let me go inside the cage for two minutes and I will show you you are wrong," said the stranger.

The ringmaster looked at him pityingly and said: "You will be crushed to death in less than three minutes."

"I knew you would say that," said the stranger smiling, "so I have brought a legal document with me which frees you from all responsibility."

When he was sure the document was authentic, the ringmaster revealed the exciting news to the public. With a lively gesture, the stranger flung off his hat and coat and said, "Now, open the gate."

Bozo stopped his continuous rotations and swivelled his bloodshot eyes towards the iron gate and began to shake when the chains were pulled. The small defenceless man entered the cage and shut the door behind him. Bozo gave a threatening trumpet of rage, but the intruder began to talk gently to him. With the first syllables, the elephant became quiet. The anxious public could not hear what was being said only Bozo seemed to understand the language. His massive voice continued caressingly. Then Bozo gave a light, childish bray and began to shake his head from side to side. The stranger drew closer and patted his long trunk, winding it round his wrist. He made the elephant turn round very slowly in the cage until the astonished audience could bear the silence no longer and broke into applause.

At last the man came out of the cage and said, "Bozo is

not a rogue at all, he was a bit homesick and so I spoke to him in Hindustani. He is an Indian elephant and that is the language he was brought up with. He will be all right now for a while." When the man had disappeared, the ringmaster examined the legal document and saw the signature – it said Rudyard Kipling.

In spite of an elephant's size it is extremely sensitive in every sphere including its nervous system. The elephants in Windsor Safari Park are terrified by the roar of planes overhead and have had to be supplied with enormous anti-accoustic earmuffs.

When you see tables in people's houses made from elephants legs and the long ivory tusks sprouting from walls like trophies, it is sad to think that in order to get them, a man has had to kill an animal that could have been one of his most faithful friends, and as affectionate to him as a dog, even capable of dying through desperation when his master dies. Would it not be wonderful if you could count the number of people on the fingers of even one hand who were prepared to die similarly?

Konrad Lorenz writes that you can never replace a loved person while you can replace animals however much you loved them. In his book *And Man met Dog* he says that if you buy a puppy of the same breed immediately after your dog has died, you will find that he will gradually usurp the place left by your old and faithful companion. He tells how his old dog Bully's life was cut short by an apoplectic fit. He suddenly regretted that Bully had no descendants to take his place. He was only seventeen and this was his first canine bereavement. Bully always used to limp because of a badly healed fracture and Lorenz would hear him trotting behind and panting. When he died, Lorenz could still hear him trotting. As soon as he began listening consciously for the footsteps and the panting, it disappeared but when was thinking of something else, the footsteps reappeared. It was only when Tito, his new dog, who was still a clumsy and comical looking puppy began trotting behind him that old Bully's spirit was finally exorcised.

For reasons of natural order, says Lorenz, man cannot remain faithful to one single dog, but he can remain faithful to the same breed. Most men continue to believe that animals are in the world solely for their own use and entertainment, and in exploiting their love, lose a unique joy – the friendship and fidelity of an animal.

A diverting statistic has been made on the intelligence of animals who cross the road. First and top comes the goose which never gets run over, next the pig, then cats, then man, then dogs and last of all hens. People can no longer make disparaging remarks about geese.

Chimpanzees

Perhaps the famed intelligence of chimpanzees derives from the fact that they can imitate man better than any other animal.

About 15 years ago the chimpanzees of St. Louis Zoo became famous the world over. There were twenty-four of them and they could do everything. Nocciolino could drive a car perfectly and Sambo ran a drinks stall and, when asked for an orangeade, would get a bottle, take the cap off, put two straws in it and hand it graciously to his customer. He also knew how to light cigars and cigarettes and blow the matches out afterwards. But foremost was Jackie who came from a rich family with very refined tastes. He wore clothes cut from the finest cloth and leant on an elegant small cane as he walked. When he was bought by the zoo, he travelled to St. Louis in a sleeping car with his new keeper, refusing to sleep anywhere that was not in a sleeping berth or in the same compartment as his new keeper.

In the middle of the night, the keeper was woken by a sound and noticed the light was on and Jackie was no longer in his sleeping berth. Worried, he was just about to get out of bed and begin looking for him when he heard the water flush in the lavatory. A few seconds later, Jackie reappeared from the lavatory, turned out the light, got into bed and pulled the covers over himself and went to sleep peacefully.

But the most exceptional chimpanzee of all was Chumley. His story is told by Gerald Durrell in *The Overloaded Ark*.

"Chumley was a full grown chimpanzee, his owner, a District Officer, was finding the ape's large size rather awkward, and he wanted to send him to London Zoo as a present, so that he could visit the animal when he was back in England on leave. He wrote asking us if we would mind taking Chumley back with us when we left. I don't think that either John or myself had the least idea how big Chumley was: I know that I visualised an ape of about three years old, standing about three feet high. I got a rude shock when Chumley moved in.

"He arrived in the back of a small van, seated sedately in a huge crate. When the doors of his crate were opened and Chumley stepped out with all the ease and self confidence of a film star I was considerably shaken for, standing on his bow legs in a normal slouching chimp position, he came up to my waist, and if he had straightened up, his head would have been on a level with my chest. This was no young chimp as I had expected but a veteran of about eight or nine years old, fully mature, strong as a powerful man and, to judge by his expression, with considerable experience of life. Although he was not exactly a nice chimp to look at, he certainly had a terrific personality.

"He stood on the ground and surveyed his surroundings with a shrewd glance and then he turned to me and held out one of his soft, pink-palmed hands to be shaken with exactly that bored expression that one sees on the faces of professional handshakers. Round his neck was a thick chain, and its length dropped over the tailboard of the lorry and disappeared into the depths of his crate. With an animal of less personality than Chumley this would have been a sign of his subjugation, of his captivity. But Chumley wore the chain with the superb air of a Lord Mayor. He seated himself in a chair, dropped his chain on the floor, and then looked hopefully at me. It was quite obvious that he expected some sort of refreshment after his tiring journey. I roared out to the kitchen for them to make a cup of tea, for I had been warned that Chumley had a great liking for the cup that cheers . . .

"I sat down opposite him and produced a packet of cigarettes. As I was selecting one a long black arm was stretched across the table, and Chumley grunted in delight. Wondering what he would do I handed him a cigarette and to my astonishment he put it carefully in the corner of his mouth. I lit my smoke and handed Chumley the matches thinking that this would fool him. He opened the box, took out a match, struck it, lit his cigarette, threw the matches down on the table, crossed his legs again and lay back in his chair inhaling thankfully, and blowing clouds of smoke out of his nose.

"Chumley's crate was placed at a convenient point about fifty yards from the hut next to a great gnarled tree stump to which I attached his chain. From here he could get a good view of everything that went on in and around the hut, and as we were working he would shout comments to me and I would reply. That first day he created an uproar, for no sooner had I left him chained up and gone into the hut to do some work, than a frightful upheaval took place among the monkeys. All these were tethered on ropes under a palm leaf shelter just opposite the hut. Chumley, after I had left him, felt bored, so looking around he perceived some sizeable rocks, arming himself with these he proceeded to have a little underarm practice. The first I knew of this was when I heard shrill screams and chatterings from the Drills and Guenons. Seizing a stick I raced down upon Chumley waving it and shouting at him, trying to appear fearsome, while all the time I was wondering what was going to happen if I tried to deal out punishment to an animal almost my own size and with twice my strength. However, to my surprise, Chumley saw me coming and promptly lay on the ground, covering his face and his head with his long arms, and proceeded to scream at the top of his voice. I gave him two cuts with the stick across his back. 'You are a very wicked animal,' I said sternly, and Chumley realising that punishment was apparently over, sat up and started to remove bits of leaf from himself. 'Arrrr-oooo,' said Chumley. He shifted forward, squatted down and commenced to roll up my trouser leg and then search my calf for any spots, bits of dirt or other microscopic blemishes.

"That night, when I carried Chumley's food and drink of tea out to him, he greeted me with loud 'hoo hoos' of delight and jogged up and down beating his knuckles on the ground. Before he touched his dinner, however, he seized one of my hands in his and carried it to his mouth. With some trepidation I watched as he carefully put one of my fingers between his great teeth and very gently bit it. Then I understood, in the chimpanzee world, to place your fingers between another ape's teeth and to do the same with his, is a greeting and a sign of trust.

"Chumley's manners were perfect: he would never grab his food and start guzzling as the other monkeys did without first giving you a greeting, and thanking you with a series of his most expressive 'hoo hoos'. Give him a bottle of lemonade and a glass and he would pour himself out a drink with all the care and concentration of a world-famous barman mixing a cocktail.

"The London Zoo's official collector arrived in the Cameroons and with great regret I handed Chumley over to be transported back to England. I did not see him again for over four months, and then I went to visit him in the sanatorium at Regent's Park. He had a great straw-filled room to live in, and was immensely popular with the sanatorium staff. I did not think that he would recognise me for when he had last seen me I had been clad in tropical kit and sporting a beard and moustache, and now I was clean-shaven and wearing the garb of a civilised man. But recognise me he did, for he whirled around his room like a dervish when he saw me and then came rushing across to give me his old greeting, gently biting my finger. We sat in the straw and I gave him some sugar I had brought for him, and then we smoked a cigarette together while he removed my shoes and socks and examined my feet and legs to make sure there was nothing wrong with them. Then he took his cigarette butt and carefully put it out in one corner of his room, well away from the straw. When the time came to go, he shook hands with me formally and watched my departure through the crack in the door."

Crows

We must not leave birds out in the scale of development, with crows as their foremost representatives.

The story of Chicago, described as the most cunning crow in the world, was told by Jean George. One day, she recounts, Chicago showed how a crow's brain functioned, beating her in shrewdness and crowning his glory with a practical joke. She had festively decorated and laid a table for a small party of eight children. There were flowers, balloons and little baskets of nuts. Twice she had to chase away the unrestrained Chicago until he decided to sit on the window sill and stare outside as if he did not care a hoot for nuts. However, Jean George knew he coveted them and was secretly looking at them out of the corner of his eye. She covered each basket with a large cup and went into the kitchen, humming.

When she returned, nearly all the baskets were on the floor and Chicago was swallowing one nut after another.

She was taken aback because the cups were still on the table and she began to watch from a hiding place. Chicago flew on to the table and took the handle of the cup in his beak and pushed it to the edge of the table until the basket fell on to the floor. Then he put the cup back in its place to hide his misdeed. When Jean George fell upon him, she gripped him by his black taffeta wings and threw him out of the window. He flew off into the distance and she could distinctly hear him laughing.

One day a large flock of crows came and tried to tempt Chicago to fly away with them but he was indecisive and refused to go. Some people might take this as a sign of affection but they are mistaken. Jean George was disillusioned by the following episode.

A smallish flock of crows came to the house one morning trying to convince Chicago to leave. While she stood at the window she heard an agitated murmuring rising from the elms and the maple trees. Wings fluttered and beat the air and a cloud of crows passed rumbling over the house but Chicago still remained.

He went round the house disconsolately, his wings and beak wide open in an agony of indecision. Suddenly she heard the "Aah-Cra" of the old mother crow high above and Chicago rose into the air. He flew on to the roof, with his eyes fixed firmly ahead, in reply to the ancient call of migration. Chicago continued to fly, two beats of the wing to the second as crows do so as not to tire themselves. Suddenly Jean George understood, the cry from the nest was not a cry of distress. The mother crow had said to her son: "Go into the house, eat as much as you can, learn as much as you can. We will come and get you in October and you will teach us the customs and habits of our dear enemy so we can stand up to them and survive."

LIKE MAN

Petros Pelican

CHAPTER 4

Like Man

If, as we said before, the 'magic of animals' chiefly takes into account the capacity animals have for behaving, at times, like human beings, then we must not omit those actions which, while not denoting any particular intelligence, are of typically human derivation.

If one looks at statistics, the one fact which stands out is that the main things animals learn from men are their vices. For example, in Jerez de la Frontera, a Spanish city famous for its sherry, some mice set up house in a cellar for more than a century and fed exclusively off sherry, maintaining perfect good health. We can only hope that our own human, heavy drinkers will never discover the unsuspected nutritious value of sherry.

Not all animals have the same possibilities as these mice. But still in the field of alcoholics, it is well known that tame chimpanzees are so diligent in their imitations of man they also copy his drinking habits and become proper alcoholics incapable even of losing the vice.

Even cows which are normally placid creatures, can become drunk and disolute through alcohol. Once, in the Beaujolais region in France an area which is rich in delicious wines, a cow use to come staggering back from the pastures every day, its breath stinking of wine. The herdsman decided to unravel the mystery and explored the field where the cow had been grazing. There he found the explanation: in a barn on the edge of the field one of the large vats used for maturing the wine had sprung a leak, and the wine was running out under the door and had formed a small stream from which the cow drank copiously, evidently finding it much better than its usual water.

Among animals which love alcohol are elephants, chiefly, as I said before, the tame ones which naturally have greater opportunities to taste it.

In a city in the United States some time ago, Jumbo, an elephant who escaped from the circus he was working in, caused a sensation when he finished up, goodness knows how, in the cellar of a wine shop, draining off all the cognac he could find. When he re-emerged, you can imagine what a state he was in. It took two hundred men to capture him over a period of 5 hours.

But not only domesticated elephants love alcohol; there are some wild ones who now manage to make it themselves. The elephants in the Kruger National Park in South Africa have discovered that if they eat fruit similar to plums, which grow on the Marula tree, and then drink a little water, they experience a very agreeable sensation. Laboratory experiments have proved that the water stimulates alcoholic fermentation in the fruit and an examination of the elephants' blood afterwards revealed traces of alcohol.

Camels, some of them at least, have a pronounced vice, that of smoking. Their drivers are aware of this penchant and always prepare a triangular piece of wood with a hole at one end like a mouthpiece which they place in the camel's mouth, lighting some tobacco on top of it. The camel closes its eyes and with a beatific air avidly inhales the smoke which puts it completely in order even when it is tired and unwilling. He then becomes lively and obliging and throws itself into its work.

Also among birds we find some leanings towards vice. The domestic corncrake belonging to Mr. Paul Sweeney of

Tout Creek in the United States, one day stole a cigarette from his master who had been smoking it and left it in an ashtray for a second. The corncrake smoked it right down to the bottom evidently enjoying it since from that moment on it began to smoke regularly.

There is a most sociable cockerel which lives in a bar on the outskirts of Granada and has become the local attraction. It begins every day with a pint of beer, then drinks apéritifs and wine with the clients in the bar and if someone offers it a cigarette, presses it between its beak, smoking it with evident pleasure. Those English birds, tits, have far more sober habits and confine themselves to piercing holes in the tops of milk bottles left outside doors and greedily drink all the cream on top.

I know a pelican called Petros whom I met several years ago in Mykonos, an Aegean island of many windmills, shimmering white houses and a deep blue sea. After a wonderful bathe in the sea, an excellent meal and a walk through the town, we drank ouzo outside the port's only bar, sitting at the tables outside.

The ambience was extraordinary: there were locals playing backgammon, English and German artists, and many long-haired Americans in blue jeans who must have been the first hippies. But the only one who came across to our table, surpassed every expectation – it was a pelican. He waddled across with a dignified and peaceful air, as if waiting to be offered something that was his due, but certainly not expecting charity. From the smiles of those around us, we knew he lived there and had not just arrived from the sea as we first thought. We offered him an olive which he politely accepted.

I asked several people about him and learned that in 1955 a great cloud of pelicans was flying to Egypt by way of the Balkans across to Africa. One of them was young, tired and wounded. Far beneath him lay the island of Mykonos. The dying bird glided down in that direction

and landed on one extremity of the island. If a passing
fisherman had not seen him and compassionately picked
him up and carried him to the harbour, he would probably
have perished.

At the harbour he was handed over to Theodoros
Kyrandodis, a sailor, who loved wild animals and kept
several birds and a small seal in his house. The pelican was
christened Petros, in honour of a Mykonos hero, Petros
Dracopoulos, who had been shot by the Nazis. Petros was
lovingly cared for and he soon recovered.

The Greeks, who are still a fatalistic people and also
somewhat superstitious, looked on Petros as a messenger
from the sky and from that moment on he became a mascot
for Mykonos. Half seriously and half jokingly, it began to
be said that after his arrival the fish catch grew more
abundant than it had been for centuries, that the god
Apollo had re-appeared in living form sending his emissary
and so on. All this was meat and drink to Petros who was
cuddled, coaxed and adored by everybody. But one day,
when he had recovered his full strength, Petros saw the
migrations of his ex-companions high up in the sky and, as
he naturally was unchained, he disappeared.

The whole island fell into an immediate uproar: the
coastguards and the police were alerted and radio messages
sent from one island to another. But Petros had evidently
become domesticated because the comforting news arrived
that he had touched down at Tinos, a neighbouring island.
It was at this point that a mini-war broke out which
entertained the whole of Greece. It was called the
Pelicanese War because Tinos refused to restore Petros to
Mykonos.

The controversy, in which rather harsh words were
exchanged between the representatives of the two islands,
was referred to the prefect of the Cyclades, who had
jurisdiction over both islands. The problem was this:
should Petros be regarded as a tame bird and therefore

belong to Mykonos or should he be regarded as a wild bird and free to go wherever he chose? After long discussions Petros was restored to Mykonos, carried back officially by the Tinos police, and he received a royal welcome. The inhabitants of the entire island left their work to welcome him back and the church bells rang out. If, in his time, Paris restored Helen, I do not believe the welcome would have been any warmer. From that moment on, Petros had a silver nameplate attached to his leg with 'Commune of Mykonos' stamped upon it. The islanders did not want to run any more risks.

After some time there was a difficult problem. Petros needed a female companion (or perhaps a male companion, because it is almost impossible even for expert ornithologists, to establish the sex of these birds). Petros was sent two companions and Mykonos went to the wedding of all three of them with Petros wearing a red tie. The vice mayor entreated the three animals to remain faithful to one another and read out the telegrams of good wishes which had arrived not only from Greece but from all over the world because the story of Petros had for some time now crossed national boundaries.

Unfortunately one of Petros' companions died almost immediately, but he was replaced by another, the gift of a French cinematographic team. The pelicans remained three but as far as I know there has been no announcement of a happy event. As the pelicans are of different species it is possible that they have not been able to mate and in the second place it seems that pelicans can only mate in large groups, and thirdly we cannot exclude the possibility that they might all three be males or all three females. In the meantime Petros amuses himself with his companions and does not suffer from any competition. He is uncontestedly the prince of Mykonos; it is he who plays football with Theodoros, he who opens doors and creeps into other people's houses, and he who wanders among the tables in the cafes drinking ouzo with the customers and sometimes jumping into the laps of young and beautiful customers which makes one suspect that he might be male. He has got used to being photographed and hardly does he see a camera pointing at him than he strikes up a pose. He has also acquired some refined tastes. The day I got to know him, I was spending the night in the open at a place where they served lobsters. Petros, attracted by the smell, since this restaurant was not on his usual route, hurried there to get some lobsters and some white wine.

Petros brought fame and fortune to Mykonos. Since his arrival luxury hotels have sprung up , postcards, statues and medals all bearing his effigy are sold and there was talk of building a church called San Petros of the Pelicans.

Pelicans eat a lot and the inhabitants of Mykonos pay a special tax for their maintenance. But they pay it willingly and hope to go on paying it for many years to come. I knew Petros in 1970 when he was not yet sixteen. Fortunately a pelican lives for about 40 years and so I hope to go and find him again soon and drink another glass of ouzo with him.

Another bad habit many animals have in common with man is that of theft; and, by that, I do not mean when a cat or a dog pinches a leg of meat from the fridge or off the table, since they do not have any concept of ownership and cannot acquire it except as a conditioned reflex and generally only through being punished. Thefts are usually completely useless to animals and they steal more for the pleasure of it. They are kind of kleptomaniacs.

One of the most thieving animals is the American wolverine, an animal similar to the marten. When it finds a tent or a hunter's cabin temporarily empty, it will go in and consciously devour all the food stocks and provisions, and then steal off with all the clothes and utensils, none of which will be of any use to it, and bury them in a far-away wood.

The so-called coconut thief, a tropical crab, is not really a genuine thief, but obtains its food in such a strange way that it is worth mentioning. It climbs up a palm tree, manages not only to make the coconuts drop down, but can also open them with its strong claws.

The robberies of the 'thieving' magpie and its passion for glittering objects are too well known to mention here. But I knew a crow whose story, like Petros', I want to tell you. It is the story of Cocco.

As I have already said, I am of the opinion that crows are among the most sensitive and intelligent animals that exist, even if at times they are rascals of the first order and amuse themselves by pulling people's legs and laughing at them behind their back. Cocco was a crow I knew very well because it lived in the garden of friends of mine, and was more than tame. He was a type of dictator but so sympathetic that everyone gave way to his caprices without a murmur. He insisted on having his meals at fixed hours, flying through the kitchen and shrieking with an indignant air; what is more he had a small vice: he was a thief, or kleptomaniac if you prefer the term. With Cocco around, nothing was safe. Cigarettes, ashtrays, envelopes, newspapers, everything and anything he could carry in his beak, disappeared. And when all the windows were open in the summer and he had free access to the house, the number of things that disappeared was enormous.

Particularly strong and resistant objects would be generally found on the roof, where Cocco had his hiding place until it was discovered: but he certainly belonged to the anti-smoking brigade since I never managed to keep a cigarette intact with him around. He carried off my packet, emptied it conscientiously and destroyed each cigarette one by one. There is nothing more frustrating for an enraged smoker to see the only packet of cigarettes he has with him reduced into minute, unsmokable crumbs, especially when there is little probability of being able to get hold of another packet on a Sunday in a house on a hill inhabited by non-smokers.

When I think back, it was probably after the visits to Cocco that I gave up smoking. Pockets were certainly not a good hiding place. It was the first place Cocco would look, if he could not see any interesting objects to hand. He would draw close furtively and suddenly – whoosh – there would go my pen, handkerchief and alas, my house keys or car keys. One day, we were all locked inside for several hours because Cocco had carried off the keys to the iron gates. Another time, a young American girl was a guest and spent nearly all her time shut up in her room studying or writing. She had, therefore, little occasion to visit Cocco. Her window gave on to the garden and she left many things on her window sill. As nobody had warned her of Cocco's habits and she was too timid to tell her hosts that some of her things were missing every morning, she must have spent many sleepless nights, thinking she had seen a phantom appear from one moment to the next.

Cocco also enjoyed doing imitations. His favourites were 'cats' and 'sirens'. You can imagine the astonishment of people the first time, when in a completely catless house, they suddenly heard very nearby, an unequivocal miaow. Or when in one of the lanes in the hills which were not very busy, one heard at different times of the day the howl of the fire engines.

Unfortunately, Cocco was always free and did not steal just in his own home. Every so often he would make an excursion to the nearest town and would return with strange objects which could not even be restored to their legitimate owners because we did not know where they came from. We would have had to put daily notices in the newspapers to announce the finding of odd socks, hankies, slippers and keys.

Like all intelligent animals, Cocco had likes and dislikes. When he found somebody to his taste, he would roost on their shoulder or their head and give them affectionate pecks. If he did not like a person, the pecks were no longer affectionate and the thefts multiplied. At mealtimes he would appear from nowhere, take his piece of meat and fly away to eat it in peace. The dogs barked at him and followed him in vain. He would turn round to look at them with his vivacious black eyes as if he were laughing at them.

I do not know what happened to Cocco in the end. He disappeared mysteriously one day and never returned. Among the possible explanations, I prefer to think that he flew after a beautiful female Cocco who was as black and as likeable as him.

I cannot omit mentioning Tintin, the Japanese barbary ape my mother kept for 9 years in a large country house and which she treated as a person. Tintin had one favourite pastime: he learnt to use keys and amused himself by locking every single one of the twenty-four rooms and all the cupboards. Then he would hide the keys and laugh. He only gave the keys back after many caresses, prayers and promises of every kind. However, we always forgave him because of his affection and incredible kindness.

At that time my mother was very young and Tintin was practically her only companion in that large country house. One evening, when she was feeling particularly melancholy, sitting in an armchair meditating sadly with Tintin settled on one arm, she suddenly felt a small hand stroking her. She looked up and saw Tintin whose eyes seemed to say, "Don't worry, it's only me and I love you."

The gorillas at Frankfurt Zoo have a television in their cage and adore watching programmes. A small local poll revealed that their favourite programmes were feature films and the football results. The most popular sports with the gorillas were car-racing, boxing and weight-lifting.

The orang-utan is another ape which has one big thing in common with modern man: it sleeps in a bed. Obviously they are not like our beds, given that the orang-utan is usually found in forests, but there are certain affinities with human beds. It is a platform on a tree made from woven branches and covered with leaves. The orang-utan has a strange peculiarity in beds; to make sure it is always fresh and that it cannot be singled out too easily by enemies, it prepares a different bed every night on different trees.

The saddest thing animals have acquired from the modern world is their attitude to neurosis or insanity. Reindeer of the Finnmark Province of Norway, for example, have had their nerves shattered by the low-flying jet planes which become more numerous with the passing of time. The poor beasts have reached such a pitch of terror and anguish through this terrible noise that they often throw themselves over cliffs or allow themselves to die of starvation. One can see how northern animals are particularly sensitive to noise because they are used to the infinite silences of ice and tundra.

White polar bears, also, are driven frantic by the sound of a horn. Fortunately, there is little occasion to hear them where they live but it was discovered by various explorers who use a type of horn to send messages from one camp to another.

The oddest case of neurosis does not concern northern animals but a cock pheasant living near Minneapolis airport which is convinced it is an aeroplane. Hardly has an aeroplane moved on to the runway and begun to taxi along, than the cock pheasant arrives from goodness knows where and flies alongside the plane at the very moment of take off. Naturally it is immediately outstripped by the plane and the pheasant runs back to be on time for the next flight.

Man, too, has several useful and amusing habits in common with animals. Cleanliness, for example. The cleanest animal is the eagle which bathes every day and would never go without it. Cleanliness in cats is also well known. Another interesting aspect is the mutual cleanliness among certain apes who consider it a correct, social ritual. It can be an expression of friendship, affection, courtship and above all, deference. It is not uncommon to witness a large male barbary ape, who is very important in his group, being closely examined for fleas by one or two females. Once the operation is over, the male ape de-fleas the females in grateful recognition.

The starling holds a live ant in its beak and passes it through its feathers to rid itself of microscopic parasites. Other birds have even more radical methods: they crawl into ants' nests not to eat the ants as one might imagine, but so that they can destroy the parasites among their feathers. This only happens with microscopic parasites which are food for ants, because slightly larger ones are a dainty dish for some small birds. Some cows know about this custom too and allow a bird to stand constantly on their backs and feed upon their undesirable guests. Parasites inhabit all wild animals and it is interesting to see what they devise to get rid of them.

But the most cunning animal is still the fox and its method of ridding itself of fleas is obviously the result of reason. It goes into the water with a branch in its mouth, conscious obviously of the fact that fleas have a great fear of drowning. Then it submerges itself so that only the tip of its muzzle is showing. When it is sure that all the fleas have climbed out on to the branch, it lets go and swims to the river bank completely free of fleas.

The principle of mutual good turns in the field of cleanliness can also be found in the field of food and it is often not so much a question of mutual favours as of rewarded theft. The classic example of this is that species of wild fowl known as the curlew, which is found nearly everywhere in the world. The curlew loves to eat algae, but not being a diver, it cannot reach it. Not wishing to forgo its favourite food, it waits until a diver bird brings some up to the surface, then snatches it from his beak. As payment, the curlew becomes a lookout and stands sentry. At the first sign of danger, it gives the alarm with its characteristic whistle, allowing the other birds to flee to safety.

It is not only between animals that this mutual aid works: there is one animal which has established this practice with man. It is the honeyguide, a strange small bird which lives in Central Africa and is very partial to beeswax. Unable to get it himself by going into a beehive, it has drawn up an agreement with the natives. It guides them to the hive where they collect the honey and in exchange hand over the honeycomb to the bird. This exchange always works and the natives are convinced that if they did not give the honeyguide its honeycomb one day, it might lead them to a nest of poisonous vipers the next time.

Revenge is one of the most widespread sentiments among animals. Some time ago in Liberia, a native killed a young gorilla by mistake and returned home without noticing any signs of danger. But several days later, when he was out hunting, he was attacked by a band of adult gorillas who had been lying in wait for him and were getting their revenge in the most violent way possible, for the death of their companion.

Anger is a sentiment we also share with many animals: the most amusing example is perhaps the llama, which anybody can test in a zoo. The llama is an extremely irritable animal and if somebody annoys it, it will spit all over that unfortunate person's face.

Even the world of song festivals has crept into the animal kingdom. Some time ago a sheep song festival took place in Val d'Orba which was open to all the sheep in Italy. The winner was the youngest participant, Kitty, a black and white sheep which in the jury's opinion and before an audience of three thousand, delivered the most harmonious bleat of the festival.

If there is one faculty that distinguishes man from animals it is an awareness of death – the consciousness that this life will sooner or later end, which biologists and zoologists say animals do not possess.

This makes the story of Corky, the terrier which

committed suicide through jealousy, all the more incredible. Corky lived with his master, a farmer, on a farm bordering on to a busy road. One day his female mate went off with another dog and later gave birth to some puppies. At first, Corky treated them as his own, licking them and playing with them, and making sure they were safely out of the road which he knew very well. Then one day he suddenly began to hate them. Perhaps he was jealous of the mother's attentions, or simply that the pups were growing larger and his instinct to protect the smallest lessened.

One day he led the puppies in the middle of the traffic and left them there as though he wished them to be run over. The puppies ran to safety and were immediately tied up. Corky retired in a corner and sulked. The next morning, the milkman told the farmer how the dog had literally thrown himself under the wheels of his car and that by some miracle he had managed to stop. Two days later, Corky threw himself under a car and this time succeeded. Could this be called an accident? Can this be rejected as consciousness of death?

As animals have their suicides, and this was only one example among thousands, so they also have their cemeteries. Everybody must have heard of the famous and legendary elephant cemetery where pachyderms take themselves to die, and where the survivors drag their dead companions if they did not manage to get there in time.

But perhaps it is not well known that among other animals of opposite dimensions this custom has become a funeral rite. Some species of desert ants patiently drag the bodies of their dead companions to the place that has been designated as their cemetery. But among their multiple activities, there is one less funereal one: in very numerous communities there is always a group of ant firemen. When a fire breaks out, the firemen ants run in a mass and spray a special kind of liquid on the flames which prevents them from flaring up and extinguishes the fire rapidly.

But here, finally, are some amusing episodes even though they were not amusing for the protagonists. The world is full of dogs that bring newspapers to their masters but a dog that is fined is exceptional. It happened to Leon, a 14-year-old dog which lived in a Spanish town. Leon used to go every day to the newspaper kiosk to pick up his master's paper and would carefully scrutinise the traffic lights before crossing the main road. One day, he was evidently distracted or his eyesight had worsened with age, because he crossed when the traffic lights were red. The policeman stopped him and wrote him out a fine which the dog, without argument, took back to his master together with the newspaper.

Another animal was even fined by the police for driving a car. It was a chimpanzee which the El Paso police found driving a car quite obviously without a driving licence. At his side sat the owner whom the police could only fine for speeding.

Who has not, as a child, and sometimes also as an adult had the temptation to pull, at least once in one's life, the communication cord on a train to see what would happen? The only time I've heard about it happened not just once but fourteen times and was done by a circus elephant that was travelling from Chicago to Downey on a train. The train was 3 hours late.

Another lucky animal is a setter which belonged to Professor Phelps of Yale and is perhaps the only dog that has ever been given credit. When he was hungry he went into a restaurant, sniffed at the food it wanted and was then served by the waiter. Professor Phelps passes by every so often to pay the bill.

And let us finish with some glory. Who but the English would attribute some glory to animals? In English seaside towns in days gone by, cats which were particularly worthy, used to be decorated with special honours.

CHAPTER 5

Aesthetic Sense of Animals

We have talked frequently about monkeys and apes but if you look more closely at apes, although they are intelligent, they cannot undertake a human activity continuously.

Of course, we have seen chimpanzees that can distribute drinks but only on request, they never do it of their own accord, as if it were their job.

But the elephant can. Perhaps we are fated to discover that instead of being descended from the apes we are descended from elephants. Perhaps this is no more than a whim of mine, but the elephant really is the only single animal with the capacity to act that comes from outside himself. In other words, it is not part of its social structure. Perhaps there is a link missing in Darwin's chain?

To make up for this missing link, however, some apes have been gifted with a sense of the aesthetic and will demonstrate it with pleasure. In his book *The Biology of Art*, Desmond Morris has reviewed the artistic work of thirty-two ape artists, of which twenty-three are chimpanzees, two are gorillas, three orang-utans and four are monkeys. But why do apes paint? There could be aesthetic reasons – perhaps the animals like to see their finished work, or may be there are utilitarian reasons too, in that the animal may have been rewarded the first time it painted a picture, and now knows that every splash and squiggle it executes will result in a new reward. When the ape sees its work and sees it is not too unpleasant it throws itself into painting willingly.

But this solution does not really stand up. Some apes become so passionate about drawing and painting that they will not be distracted for any reason. The designs painted by apes for their own pleasure are very different from those of the utilitarian apes. Utilitarian types of apes confine themselves to scrawling and pay no attention to design because they know any scribble will be sufficient to obtain the promised banana or whatever else. The others, instead, put a good deal of effort into their work and clearly have some idea of the effect they want to achieve.

It is interesting to note that when a child draws a picture, it imitates life, while apes, who are nature's finest mimics, depict nothing realistic at all in their pictures, but go more for abstracts and vague geometrical designs. Another artistic difference between apes and men is that while primitive man used a few colours only, apes tend to use an enormous quantity, taking nearly everything there is to hand.

When an ape has finished its picture, it is impossible to make him continue. If it is forced to do so, it flies into a rage and begins to draw random lines all over his picture, as if it wanted to erase it. When an ape is choosing a picture, its precise tastes give it a strong preference in picking out symmetrical designs. When the drawings of apes were shown to child psychologists specialising in analysing children's drawings, they have always been analysed as the work of schizoid or paranoid children. Psychologists have never been mistaken in telling an ape's sex through its pictures and since man has a tendency to schizophrenia, there is no reason why apes should not also. It is not only apes who possess an aesthetic sense. Nearly all animals are gifted with it.

Closing the psychological brackets, we can see, adding everything up, that some apes do devote themselves in effect to human activities, but no one has yet seen an ape sweep the floor of his cage or sew up the hem of its clothes, or chop firewood. We must deduce from this that the unique activity apes are capable of is an artistic one; and one that is free and not subject to any law or imposed on them by an external will.

To sew a hem, an ape must be shown what to do so it can learn and it will do so but it will never do it without being told. But drawing pictures which are not imitative, all that is needed is to let him develop what is in his mind, and which will be different each time he paints. Even here there is a great need for freedom and to design what they want is a way of being free. I would deduce from this that if apes do not learn to work it is for the same motives that men do not work unless they have to – and this is simply that whether free or imprisoned, apes have no need to work.

In her *Book of Cats* Jehanne Jean-Charles tells how her kitten went mad about a Vivaldi record and discovered that, by putting the pick-up back to the beginning of the record, it could listen to the music again. It did this so many times that the record was soon worn out. Another of her cats loved to run up and down the piano keyboard to play the sounds that fascinated it. There are numerous other examples of chickens producing more eggs or of cows yielding more milk with music in the background.

The seal is one of the animals which can be most easily tamed and which also has several affinities with dogs. The English call it a sea-lion but would have done better to call it a sea-dog. In order to rear a seal, you naturally need some water in the neighbourhood where the animal, which is clumsy and awkward on land, can elegantly execute its acrobatic evolutions.

But it is not any more difficult to raise a small seal than a puppy. If it has been orphaned it will soon get used to a feeding bottle and will claim it with cries, which, if not immediately answered, turn into small, demanding barks.

Like a puppy, a small seal learns to climb into its adoptive parents' laps and it is difficult to get it out of the habit, especially when it is still young and weighing several stone, and it continues to think of itself as a puppy and, as such, endowed with all privileges. Just like a dog, it is difficult to convince a seal that it should sleep in the kitchen instead of its parents' bed, and if the parents are soft-hearted they will give way to its requests after two or three hours in order to get some sleep themselves.

On the other hand, a seal can reward those who love it, by its acute intelligence. It learns quickly not to make a mess in the house and can pull its towel out when it comes back from a swim and stretch out on it until it is perfectly dry.

Seals love music enormously and it would be a wonderful quality in them if they did not decide to take part in concerts. Rowena Farr writes about this in her book *Seal Morning*.

"Since ancient times it has been known that seals are attracted by music and singing and Lora's musical talent came out early. Whenever Aunt Miriam and I struck up on the piano Lora would wriggle over to the instrument, lean against it or (more inconveniently) the player's legs and listen with an expression of intense concentration and joy, swaying now and then with her whole body to the music. When the music stopped, she would sit quietly for several minutes, still under its spell.

"One day I started singing 'Men of Harlech' Lora let out a loud groan and broke into a roar. Seals have perhaps the largest vocal range among mammals. Their repertoire includes grunts, snorts, barks, peculiar mewing, hisses and a wail which often rises from a deep bass to a treble.

"She began to pester me for my mouth organ and attempted to wrest it from me by playing it. I finally acknowledged defeat and placed it in her mouth. She found to her annoyance that it emitted no sound in spite of being gnawed with vigour. She started tossing it up into the air and catching it as though it were a ball but all to no effect. Taking the instrument in her mouth, she gave a loud sigh of desperation. This produced a blast of noise from the mouth organ and galvanised Lora to fresh efforts.

"I set off for a walk. When I returned, there were most curious sounds coming from the rear of the loft. Lora had learnt the blow-suck method and there she was blowing and sucking feebly in a state of almost complete exhaustion, for she had been doing this apparently, ever since I had left her.

"A young friend of mine after visiting us, sent her a toy trumpet. Lora soon learnt to render ear-splitting blasts on this when it was held for her. Another admirer sent her a small xylophone complete with beater and she would hold the beater in her teeth and bang any note to which I pointed.

"Her self-imposed practising on these various instruments drove us almost to distraction at times. It became necessary to put them out of her reach and allow her to play them only for short periods in the evenings. An unfortunate result of the singing lessons I had given her was that now whenever Aunt or I began to play the piano, Lora, were she in the vicinity, would immediately lift her head and wail fortissimo. It is well nigh impossible to struggle through a Brahms sonata with a seal singing at the top of its voice. So most of our playing had to be done when she was in the lochan.

"Visitors to the croft could never understand why we would not let Lora play and sing for hours on end, which she would have been perfectly happy to do if given the chance. Although they would tell us in their letters that they were looking forward immensely to the quiet of the wilderness, the rude shattering of this quiet by Lora in one of her recitals did not appear to worry them in the least. On the contrary they enjoyed every minute of it and were as disappointed as she was when they were brought to an abrupt close by Aunt or myself. . . .

"After a time we were forced to the rather humiliating conclusion that friends came on visits mainly to get acquainted with Lora; our company, peace and quiet, the beauties of the countryside were little more than sidelights.

" 'Where is she?' a guest would ask, the moment he had dumped down his suitcase and gulped a cup of tea to revive himself after the rigours of the journey.

" 'Out in the lochan.'

"The guest would take a quick look at the rolling sea of hills, rocks and pockets of water stretching in every direction to the far horizon, and then 'Well . . . can't she be got in?'

"We would stroll down to the lochan, the guest carrying the trumpet in readiness and we would stare across the sheet of water, devoid of any sign of animal life. I would call and presently we would see the small, dark speck of her head coming towards us, with perhaps a smaller one nearby belonging to an otter. In less than a minute she would be ashore and, the trumpet pressed against her mouth, give a rendering of 'Danny Boy'. Her boisterous good nature and love of showing off before visitors made her ever ready to play.

"A certain uncle of mine took a great fancy to her. At his home outside Aberdeen he used to hold monthly ceilidhs (musical evenings) at which local talent used to perform. Uncle Andrew became obsessed with the idea that Lora should be a guest at one of these ceilidhs.

"On the evening of the ceilidh, I led her into the drawing room where it was to be held. My feelings about the forthcoming proceedings were dubious. A well-known singer of mouth music (unaccompanied singing) was coming and had consented to start the evening with a song. A melodeon player was to take the platform next, followed by

Lora giving an exhibition of xylophone playing. That was to comprise the first half of the evening.

"There would be a break for supper. During the second half, amongst other attractions, Lora was to sing to my piano accompaniment. So far so good.

"The guests started to arrive. Lora the most sociable and extroverted of creatures, greeted them warmly. I suggested to Uncle that I should shut Lora, in his study until it was her turn to perform. But he and several of the guests vetoed this suggestion at once. She must stay. The singer smiled charmingly and started off with the assurance of a professional. She managed to sing a few notes of an old Hebridean air before the inevitable happened; Lora raised her head and roared her way from a deep bass to a seal top C. Even a full Covent Garden chorus would not have been able to compete with that, and the singer wisely gave up there and then. The audience were hysterical with laughter. They had not heard anything as good as that for a long while. When a certain amount of calm had been restored someone suggested that Lora be allowed to perform first and the human faction later; thus she would get her little act off her chest and be willing to listen to others. It was blatantly apparent that he had no knowledge of seals whatsoever, but by then she was out of my hands and being stage-managed by others. She was lifted bodily on to the top of the piano by two stalwart males so that the audience would get a good view of her, and the xylophone was placed before her. I stood by her side ready to point to the notes in case she should be overcome by a sudden fit of nerves at the sight of so large an audience and momentarily forget her piece. My presence proved unnecessary. She took the beater from me and started off with aplomb on 'Baa-Baa Black Sheep'. The audience strained forward. I caught murmurs of 'Yes, I recognise that bit'.

" 'Quite incredible', and 'Isn't she playing "Danny Boy" now?'

" 'No, I'm sure she isn't. Oh perhaps she might be.'

"Loud applause greeted the final slither of the beater along the length of the instrument which denoted the end of 'Danny Boy' and was followed by vociferous calls for an encore.

" 'Carry on,' said Uncle beaming at me.

"I thought the front row, consisting of the other prospective performers looked a trifle discouraged at the way things were going. I announced 'Where My Caravan has Rested'.

" 'I used to sing that as a subaltern in the First World War,' a charming grey-haired gentleman confessed to the room at large. 'My wife always . . .' we never heard what. Lora got off to a speedy start whacking notes left, right and centre. The caravan had apparently got loose from its moorings and was rushing towards a head-on collision. There was a loud crash as the xylophone fell to the floor, pushed off by Lora's exuberant playing. The audience rose to its feet. After a short pause in which to recover their breath, people uttered more fulsome exclamations of delight."

I wanted to dwell a while on this episode of Lora's life because I was speaking of the aesthetic sense in animals and this shows what can be obtained from an animal that is supposed to be wild, if one gives them a bit of understanding. No one has ever seen or heard a dog playing a trumpet, but a seal at least has done it. If I lived for a thousand years, I would never be able to get a single, articulate sound out of any instrument, and I am full of admiration for Lora. She disappeared in the lochan one day. Her body was never found but it is rather beautiful to imagine that she found her life-long companion, also a musician, and that today they are living happily together, singing in harmony.

But talking of Lora I do not want to leave whales out of this discussion. They show more or less the same musical tendencies, even though it is rather more difficult to keep them in a house and raise them as puppies.

Roger Playne, a scientist who studied under the auspices of Rockefeller University in the waters around Bermuda, has proved that whales sing by issuing sounds like electronic music although more musical. These whales sang for half an hour and their song has been recorded. The records have had a tumultuous success in the United States. We have known for some time that cetaceans make sounds and we now know that fish do as well. Who knows how many records and cassettes featuring octopuses or soles as star singers, will appear in the future?

LOVE · REPRODVCTION.

Rhinoceros.

CHAPTER 6

Love and Reproduction

Doctor Carlos F. a ruthless and fanatical hunter from Turin, often told his friends about the time he nearly gave up hunting. During a safari in Tanzania on a lion hunt, four or five lionesses were rambling about the area quite peacefully, although fortunately they and their young were untouchable. The male of the pride was killed, however, and the hunters waited until they could take away the skin. But one of the lionesses, almost certainly the dead lion's mate, dashed towards the body and began to lick it all over trying to bring it back to life. When she had established there was nothing more she could do, she curled up beside him, lamenting and remained there throughout the night and the following day, keeping a moving funeral wake.

That lion is now a sumptuous carpet in a mountain villa and the hunter has added the skins of many other animals. His unique, brief act of remorse was not followed by other similar feelings.

We will leave out the numerous cases where cats and dogs have returned to their owners, journeying over enormous distances which is described as homing instinct, instead of affection and loyalty which certain animals are capable of showing to man and other animals.

After the legendary dog of Ulysses which waited to die until his master returned home and was the only one to recognise him, one of the first historical dogs is Mary Stuart's spaniel. He was deeply attached to the Queen and never left her side. When she was beheaded, they found him howling desperately among the bloody folds of her dress.

Thisbe, a Maltese puppy, which belonged to Marie Antoinette is also famous because on the day the Queen was guillotined, the dog killed himself by jumping into the River Seine from the Pont St. Michel in Paris.

Psychosomatic medicine which is increasing today, shows that nearly all physical disturbances are caused by psychic complaints and is almost certainly applicable to animals as well. As far as dogs are concerned, this episode which happened several years ago in Fidenza confirms it. The protagonist was a beautiful German sheepdog which was the best friend and companion of a young man who had been seriously ill since his childhood and who was in a wheelchair for many years. The illness got worse and the young man died. Several days later the dog suddenly became blind in an extreme subconscious attempt (according to the psycho-analytical explanation) to refuse to face a reality that was too unkind and unpleasant.

Sometimes, though not often, men reciprocate this affection and devotion to their animals. A rich English land-owner left his heirs £100,000 provided that they fed his dog a steak every morning and gave him tea with sugar at five o'clock every afternoon. In a small Californian town, a man has erected a stone in memory of his dog which died saving its master's life when he had been bitten by a poisonous snake.

The legendary enmity between cats and dogs, for example, can easily be set aside when one or the other is in serious danger. The protective instinct is much stronger than any feeling of hostility. One significant episode happened some time ago in England. In a road full of traffic, a cab ran over a cat leaving it wounded and senseless, and in mortal danger from the continually passing cars. Before anyone could act, a dog arrived at top speed, grasped the cat by the nape of its neck and carried it to safety at the roadside.

A similar episode happened in Italy, in Pessina, a small provincial village in Varese, where everybody knew each other including all the animals. An old deaf cat was one day sleeping peacefully in the middle of the street, when a lorry appeared in the distance. A German sheepdog, which evidently was aware of the cat's deafness, ran into the road and carried the cat off the street before it could be run over.

Affection between animals of the same species can go to incredible lengths. There is a significant episode in which two monkeys, male and female shared the same cage in a Paris zoo. One day, the female fell ill and died, and her companion remained a long while stroking her body. Then, when he was convinced she was dead, he covered his eyes with his hands and stayed in the same position for days, refusing food until he too finally died of starvation.

An interesting field in connection with affection among animals and between animals and men, is that of adoption. In his masterpiece, *King Solomon's Ring*, Konrad Lorenz explains the conduct of goslings, those small feathery creatures, which adopt the first object, alive or inanimate, they see when they first open their eyes. The pages on his pet goose, Martina, are also very entertaining.

Adoption takes place between all animals although it is more frequent among birds. There is no shortage of stories like Romulus and Remus, Tarzan and the famous wolf children of which we still find traces every so often in forests and mountains today. Periodically, newspapers publish stories of cats which have adopted orphaned puppies or vice versa. The public feels much closer to cats and dogs, and there is far greater interest in them than in wild animals.

Two campers once captured a small orphaned owl and

took it with them whenever they moved. One morning, before feeding him, they noticed his crop was already full and thought he had managed to catch a mouse all on his own. But as this happened every morning the two campers began spying on the little owl to discover his secret. It seemed that each day before his human parents fed him, the owl got hungry and would utter sharp shrieks. Two huge adult owls would then dive down upon him, fill his beak with food and fly away. They were 'foreign' owls from an adjacent territory but they were unable to remain insensitive to the cry of a young and hungry owl.

Scientists have now come to the conclusion that among mammals, individual adults can easily adopt young, even those belonging to another species, if they are enjoying tranquil conditions themselves and not suffering from starvation. A starving lion will always leap on a gazelle, even a newly-born one, but a lioness, who is feeding her cubs in quiet conditions and is well-fed herself, can easily suckle a small, orphaned gazelle rather than leave it to die of hunger.

This protective behaviour has a scientific explanation: all young mammals have rounded jawbones which are a kind of international passport: any adult animal recognises this and will include the young outside in its own family.

People who have kept animals for some time and grow fond of them must be careful when they introduce new animals into the house. It can work if the new arrival is a pup. Then the pup will probably be adopted by the other animal, even if it is of another breed. If there are a lot of animals already, things are much simpler because the affection is divided. But people who take animals in only a short while after another, with only a slight age gap between them, will find the first becomes irremediably neurotic.

It is a mistake that I have made myself and I would like as many people as possible to avoid this, especially for the good of their animals.

A couple of years ago, my beautiful Siamese cat died at

the age of twelve. It was adored by the whole family and even had its own private room. As Lorenz advises people to fill the empty space, I bought a new and tiny kitten of the same breed. It was a 2-month old Siamese and one of the most gracious creatures you can imagine. Little 'Penny' was an unchained devil and immediately conquered everyone, although she was less beautiful than the previous cat and had the rather desperate air of all cats which come from shops. With some care and a proper diet, the stunted-looking cat that had arrived, was a marvel after a month. She was bursting with health, ate abundantly and appeared to belong to the special race of flying Siamese which terrorise curtains, cardigans and the backs beneath them. But a small kitten is vivacious and needs to give vent to its feelings and 'Penny's' vitality did not suffer any frustrations. One of her favourite games was to have a ball thrown for her and to bring it back like a perfect little retriever. When she was tired she would stretch out on someone's stomach and begin to purr, and beware anybody who moved.

One day she had a slight accident which frightened us all because she seemed to be suffocating. It was not serious but, advised by friends, I decided that it might perhaps be better to have two cats instead of one. They could keep each other company and if there was an accident then at least I would still have one cat.

I searched for a small male but it was impossible to find one and on March 3, 1973, Thai entered the household. She was scarcely 2 months old and tucked away in the corner of a cage in the shop, rejected by everyone because her fur was not very soft and she did not seem very strong. I took her in my hand and she purred with the intensity of a steam engine. Love was born. During the journey back in the car she remained with her face in my overcoat pocket the whole time, purring incessantly. Penny had been with us now for a month and a half and was 4 months old. It was tragedy – hisses, bristling fur, waving tails and a mien that said "this is an intruder". All that first week Penny chased her outside. I am still convinced she meant no harm to the little kitten since she had pronounced maternal instincts, but did so because she was afraid of this small kitten which tranquilly ignored her. Slowly, they learned to eat from the same plate, then they played together attached to two different leads so they could be separated if fierce fighting broke out. But this never happened. After a week of hissing and tail waving, an ardent and deep love grew up between the two. The older cat took the little one under her protection and there were kisses, embraces, furious lickings and friendly games. But Penny was never the same again. The interest and affection shown to the little one on its arrival had created a psychological block that would probably be with her for ever. She became extremely nervous and sometimes intentionally dirtied the other cat's litter box; if she was on somebody's lap, the slightest movement was enough to make her jump up and go away, offended and convinced that nobody wanted her. On the other hand, she does not stick her claws out any more and only in play when she does and has never scratched anyone. She will lie on my mother's stomach and purr. Now she is two-and-a-half years old but it is difficult to cure her psychic disturbance because in spite of all my efforts, everybody who sees the little kitten falls madly in love with her, even though, according to the canons of Siamese beauty, Penny is much more beautiful. Having had a happy childhood, Thai is psychically very stable and stays with anyone, will let herself be picked up and stroked like a puppy. The two cats adore each other: they sleep paw in paw, so much so that they look like one cat with two heads. But it is mainly the older cat which adores the little one even though she was the innocent cause of her trauma. And woe to anyone that divides them even for a few minutes. Penny lets out threatening howls as if she were being hung, drawn and quartered and when the little kitten is given back to her, there are endless kisses and licks.

There is one story of animal jealousy in which the animal involved comes out morally way beyond many human beings. It concerns a magnificent German sheepdog which lived with, and was dearly loved by, a young married couple. When the couple had a baby, the dog began to be neglected: no more walks, no more runs in the field, no possibility of barking joyfully in case he woke the baby. The little intruder must have seemed a real Egyptian plague to the dog. No one would have blamed him if he had hated the baby. Instead he pined away when he could have made his rival disappear by using his strong, sharp claws. One day, the baby was sleeping peacefully in its cradle, the father was away and the mother was in the garden. Miserable and ignored by everybody the dog was on its own. Suddenly the young mother heard him arrive running – something he had not done for a long time. She looked up and saw the baby clasped firmly in the dog's mouth. Her immediate thought was that, in his jealousy, he had killed the baby and before she could control herself, she fainted. The dog delicately placed the baby on her stomach and licked the mother awake to arouse her attention. When she finally came to, she saw the baby safe and sound but the house in flames. The dog had gripped the baby by its shawl and carried it to its mother, forgetting about the rivalry and remembering only that this was the puppy of his friends. The dog's action was doubly heroic because while it clearly knew the flames would have killed the baby, it also knew it would have been completely innocent if the baby had died, and perhaps he would have regained some of the lost affection if their child had died. Moral: for those wanting two animals or an animal and a child together, they should get the two animals at the same time or after the baby.

Talking of animals which love, we must rid ourselves of a commonplace mistake. Although doves sometimes bill and coo, they are by no means perfect spouses. On the contrary, they are quarrelsome, unfaithful and violent. But exemplary couples can be found among animals which are usually ignored from this point of view, such as crows, owls and geese. The most harmonious couples are eagles which, when paired up, remain faithful 'until death them do part'. Widowed rooks never take another mate.

Love rituals of animals are doubtless one of the most varied sectors of zoology. With their limited possibilities animals can teach man several things about fantasy and originality. Flirting, courtship and seduction are certainly not human inventions. They have existed since the first two creatures of different sexes appeared on this earth.

Let us look at how some animals choose and win their future mates. With some species an almost feminist movement exists because the female chooses the male she prefers, surrounding him with cajolery and tenderness. Another 'young maiden' gifted with great initiative, although not exactly tender and delicate, is the female rhinoceros. When a possible suitor is in sight, she does not wait for him to approach and manifest his intentions, but charges him with her head down, hitting him all over several times, leaving him astonished and staggering. If the male appreciates the treatment and survives the encounter, they become engaged. It is difficult to imagine the reasons for such an approach; the only possible explanation can be that the two future spouses want to measure their respective strengths so that in future they can stand up to dangers and overcome them.

Apart from man, birds are among the most exhibitionist creatures in the world. It is well-known that some species grow more beautiful while courting and assume shining colours, just like men and women putting on their best clothes at the prospect of an interesting conquest. But there are other more difficult and more dangerous forms of exhibitionism. The commonest is fighting. The female of certain species do not have any choice and are won by the strongest and have to mate with them whether they like them or not. There are more liberal animals which, having fought over the same female, give her the final choice.

To impress their females, black winged stilt birds choose a part of a field as large as a plate with no grass and gather there with the other males. When the female spectator arrives, the wooers begin fighting but it is a sham fight – a tournament in which no blood is shed and which is conducted in a sporting way. The participants flap their wings and peck each other with their beaks until the female decides to enter the arena. They then stop fighting, flop down on the ground and wait for her to make her choice. She does this by making an exploratory walk around them, examining each one until she finally touches the ruff of the male she prefers.

Gifts are not just man's invention, but are used by certain species of animals and can be divided into three types: the useful gift like food, which is eaten as a sign of acceptance; the useless but decorative gift in vogue among the more evolved animals; and the useful gift which is accepted but not consumed.

One species of gnat offers his female an edible present, wrapped elegantly in a small ball of silk or saliva. Other more romantic gnats offer a basket containing not food but flowers, petals or an empty but glittering and attractive basket.

The male of one species of spider, evidently practical types, go in search of their future companions towing a piece of web containing a fly along behind them. If the female accepts the gift, a wedding takes place.

One of the more interesting rituals is that of the penguin. The male finds a pebble which it places in front of the female it wants to conquer. If she begins playing with it and pushes it here and there, it means the male has some hope;

if, having examined it carefully, she picks it up in her beak, then her acceptance is complete.

One of the most suggestive manifestations of love is dancing, especially that of the peacock. This beautiful animal which is conceited like no other, weaves a graceful dance in front of its loved one, which together with its splendid colours produces an incredible spectacle.

Less beautiful but far more sensitive are female ravens whose love habits are similar to humans. During the engagement period, the couple enjoy a certain amount of freedom in which they can try out different partners even if they, in their turn, are betrothed. But once the coupling has taken place the marital fidelity of both birds is sacred.

One bird which faces many difficulties in conquering a female is the kingfisher. An ornithologist tells how he once saw a courtship ritual lasting 4 days because of the reluctance of the shy female. The male emerged victorious with less feathers than before after a 3-hour fight with his two rivals, when he conquered the female by right. But his difficulties did not come from his defeated rivals but from the female herself who, instead of welcoming the victorious warrior, chased him away. After 3 days of rejection, the kingfisher decided to try another method and showered her with gifts.

Executing brilliant turns in the air, he dived ably into the water, rapidly speared a fish and offered it to his beloved. But not even this tactic brought the right response and once again the poor bird was rudely chased away. He dropped the fish near the female hoping she could not resist the temptation to eat it, but still she turned her head away. Again, he picked up the fish and repeated the performance twelve times but with no response. Then once again he changed tactics. No longer seeking to conquer her affections, he tried to astound her with an ostentatious display of his ability and wealth.

He began fishing frantically, seeking out the most

delicious fish and placing them beside her as our ancient courtesans would offer caviare and champagne. In a short while he had caught more than thirty fish and finally won her through his perserverance. The female lifted her head and took a small fish and flew off. The male showed his joy by swooping in large circles in the air and uttering deafening shrieks. Then he began to offer her the fish directly and they were finally accepted.

But there were valid reasons for this initial prudery. Before choosing the father of her young, the female kingfisher wanted to be quite sure he was tenacious and pugnacious and able to provide food in quantity. She was perfectly right because once she has laid her eggs, her life and that of her unhatched young are in continual danger. The nest is built in a tunnel with only one exit where the mother and young are easy prey to weasels, mice and snakes.

Some romantically-inclined spiders, instead of offering flies from their webs, offer themselves with a complicated dance of pirouettes. Crabs also dance waving their coloured legs in a clumsy way but one that is clearly attractive to the female crab. The scorpion takes his beloved 'by the hand' and walks her out – backwards.

The serenade, that delicious homage which has disappeared from man's life, still has its place in the love life of some animals. It remains difficult to imagine the love song of a crustacean even though the crayfish manages to sing in several ways by cracking its pincers together and the prawn produces a kind of song, croaking a brief serenade by rubbing his antennae against its beak. But those with the most beautiful and varied gift of song are the birds. And they also give significant and quite explicit gifts. The wren, for example, offers twigs which is a clear allusion to its future nest, and sometimes even begins building it, hoping to tempt the female by showing her the foundations of a future home.

In this sphere, the king of courtesans is the bird-of-paradise which is a proper casanova-on-the-wing. It builds an entrancing little house, 2 metres high by 4½ metres wide and decorates it with flowers, leaves and berries and the prettiest sparkling things it can find. It is difficult for a female to resist the fascination of such a pretty and carefully prepared nest, but the male's attentions do not finish there. The female bird-of-paradise has blue eyes and when her companion brings her presents, he chooses exclusively blue pebbles, blue berries and blue flowers.

There is one type of sparrow that has an interesting manner of courting. It offers its beloved a fruit, generally a cherry, trying to place it in her beak. If she does not accept his proposition then she refuses the fruit. If she consents, she accepts it but does not eat it. She keeps it for a moment, then in turn places it in the beak of her courtier. At this point, the two birds sit side by side on a branch and continue to exchange this token of love for a while.

Even during mating, there are infinite varieties and peculiarities. In hatching the eggs and rearing the young, behaviour is more varied again. The strangest pairing takes place among fish and insects and at times seems absurd. The female Ceratias Holbeoelli fish is at least ten times larger than the male which, during copulation, attaches itself in such a way that makes it look like a large pimple.

The most dramatic pairing without a doubt is that of the spider. In some species the male is infinitely smaller than the female, which after the nuptials, calmly eats her lover. This is why the variety of large tropical spider is commonly known as the black widow. The male has one way of saving itself: if the female manages only to get a leg instead of the whole spider, and it comes off, the spider limps away, mutilated but saved. Another species of spider, evidently educated in the school of experience, protects itself often saving its own life by offering the female an insect to devour during the mating. This cunning trick has not yet been discovered by the male praying-mantis which always gets eaten after the nuptials.

Another strange habit is that of the Scandinavian salmon. Before the nuptials, the female, without knowing who her future spouse will be, begins to prepare her 'nest'. While it is being built, any salmon that approaches is ferociously attacked. When the nest is finished, the female waits until a male approaches and after insemination, gives him total responsibility for guarding the territory around her nest.

Black Molly, a beautiful, black, velvety smooth fish, often seen in aquariums, deposits a quantity of eggs from which two hundred young are born. But the unnatural mother eats them immediately and rarely leaves more than four or five alive.

The scrub fowl which lives in Australia is too lazy to sit on its eggs like its cousins and deposits them in a hole which it covers with leaves and then abandons. The decaying leaves produce sufficient heat to hatch the eggs. So this animal invented a system of artificial incubation probably long before man had ever thought of it.

The gull is decidedly a creature of habit: the female lays three eggs at a time and never more. If a fourth egg is laid in her nest she will immediately push it out. It is not unusual for the father to co-operate in hatching the eggs and there are several examples including the famous one of seahorses whose female deposits their eggs in a pouch on the male's tail leaving him to hatch them out.

Among penguins, co-operation is the result of reason and free choice. After the eggs have been laid, male and female take alternate turns to sit on the nest because it is surrounded by other penguins who at the first sign of negligence, take possession of the eggs and eat them. An almost pathetic and difficult habit all fin-footed creatures, like seals and sea-lions have, is that, wherever they happen to be at the time of reproduction, they return to the place they were born even if it means covering enormous distances with great difficulty.

Among the peculiarities of reproduction, the oyster is completely hermaphrodite possessing all the male organs as well as the female organs. Animals which sit on their eggs the least are the skylark and the Australian zebra finch. Their eggs hatch out after only 11 days. The crab's reproduction is very strange: coupling can only take place when they moult their shells. Then the shell of the female dissolves in the warm water and she pulls out her legs and antennae which were previously imprisoned. She is completely defenceless against various dangers like fish, turtles and dolphins and hastens to find a companion before her shell hardens again.

The hermit crab also faces many difficulties during reproduction. In fact, besides having to find a companion, it also has to find another shell in which to live because its own has become too small. When it finds a female it drags her behind it, gripping on to her with its claws and then the mating begins. It is an extremely difficult task because the two have to come out of their shell and are so delicate that a grain of sand or a fish fin brushing past them can kill them.

The unhappiest lovers of all are oysters. Nailed to a rock without hope of moving, love for them is nothing more than a collective act, fulfilled blindly and deprived of any individuality. When the water is about 26°C and the tide is quite high, the males open their valves and project millions of sperm into the water; the females in their turn, still nailed to the rocks, open their own valves and let out their eggs. Sperm and eggs meet on neutral ground, after which the fertilised egg settles on fields of plankton.

But not all marine births are the result of mating. Sea anemones those splendid flowers which grow on the seabed, reproduce by fission. Every fragment finds a place to settle on and in a short space of time gives way to a new individual. There are certain hydrozoa which produce small transparent jellyfish, instead of eggs, which when they are fully developed, lay eggs from which perfect individuals emerge. This is really indirect reproduction. The birth and growth of the young ones of this strange marine animal is extremely interesting. The newborn are so unlike their parents that a layman would not recognise them.

The newborn crab has a long beak, feathery scales and large sentimental eyes. Newborn oysters are just like peas with a small wreath of sparkling hair. Baby oysters, unlike their manacled parents, can move about the sea freely for a fortnight until their fluctuating hair begins to secrete a liquid which becomes a type of cement and attaches them firmly to the rocks like their parents. Little by little, passing through a series of metamorphoses, they become miniature oysters, assuming their definitive form.

The female bat is the only animal which can store male sperm to use when it is convenient. Bats generally mate in the autumn but only the following spring does the female's copulation begin and the egg become fertilised. It is clear that, having discovered this, scientists are now trying to discover the secret of retarded fertilisation to use it either in artificial insemination of animals or as a cure for human sterility.

At the beginning of summer, the bats go into their maternity ward while the males assemble. It is these colonies of bats in lofts and belfries in the summer which inspire such fear in women. They are none other than groups of inocuous females waiting to give birth.

The most fantastic copulation belongs to ants. In ant communities, the virgin princesses are bred with great care and particular diets as they are destined for copulation and queen ant stature. These special ants, like the males that fertilise them, are given wings to mate in the air. Immediately after mating, their unique mission is accomplished, and they fall dead to the ground. But the most incredible thing is that the females remain fertilised all their lives and retire underground, now becoming nothing more than machines to give birth to eggs. All their lives they are assisted by their spinster sisters.

A few words must be written about the seahorse which is a graceful animal that has fascinated man since time immemorial. Its reproductive system is very interesting, beginning with the first tentative approaches. Courting consists of a complicated nuptial dance which lasts from 24 to 48 hours. The two seahorses move around one another in circles with the female pursuing the male, accompanying the proceedings with slight noises, similar to those of a tambourine. Then a true nuptial embrace follows during which the female deposits one or more eggs in the incubating pocket of the male. The embrace is repeated continuously until the female has laid 200 to 600 eggs in the male's pouch, which are fertilised the moment they are transferred. From that moment on the female's task is complete; responsibility for the eggs is now entrusted to the male whose incubating sac becomes larger and larger rather like a pregnant woman's womb. After 45 days the first seahorse is born. It is microscopic but identical to its parents except for the transparency of its body which is such that you can see its heart beating. Then the colour appears.

After the first two or three seahorses are born the father expels all the others in one violent labour spasm. They are held together in a compact mass in an air bubble. While the masses rise up to the surface, the small ones group together in fifties and sixties at a time. In antiquity, occult powers were attributed to this strange animal, and even today the Chinese believe it is an infallible remedy against old age.

One of the most romantic love processes is that of the saturnine butterfly. The male flies in front of his chosen one, spreads his wings out fully and waves his antennae; when she gives a sign of assent, he tucks his head in in a perfect bow and envelopes her antennae with his wings. But that is not all. As an extreme refinement, nature has placed little sacs containing a type of perfume on the male's front wings, part of which gets on to the sensitive antennae of the female during the embrace and this delicate homage conquers her completely.

Our old friend, the cricket has his own particular way of paying court. He begins with a serenade whose song we all know well, which grows louder and louder during his lovemaking. The courted female stays to listen and every so often gives the male a small push to encourage him. When the male has finished singing, he raises his wings; if the female is moved by his song, she jumps on to his back and sucks a delicious substance from a small gland on his wings. When she has finished eating, they are ready to mate.

In their affinity with man in the amorous field, the rather wearisome habit certain lovers have of using baby talk is widely used among females of various species of birds, which accept the attentions of males with infantile chirpings. Even the engagement period is widely used among birds: robins for example start 'going steady' in December or January but do not mate or think about building a nest until the end of March. Magpies and ducks become betrothed a year before they reach sexual maturity and mate. Swans become steady couples very quickly, are monogamous and famous for being faithful to each other all their lives.

One of the most problematical matings is that of the mole: there are, in fact, far more male moles than females. To find a companion means having to win her at a high price by fighting violent battles, and once she is conquered to mount perpetual guard over her.

The female mole waits patiently for the godlike judgement to be decided while the moles fight and she is ready to follow the winner, recognising him as having an indisputable right over her. Then the couple retire to his or her house. The male first digs a supplementary gallery which is different from the others, because it does not have an exit and is clearly constructed to hide something or someone. This is a necessary precaution because many of the other males remain single and begin to look round the den hoping to find the female alone. When a male that is more foolhardy than the rest manages to get into the den, all the husband can do is fight for his bride again. But at this point, there is another danger, while the two fight, a third suitor can creep in and steal the female. At this point we see how useful a gallery without an exit is. The female is left in the gallery awaiting the outcome of the fight.

MATERNITY

Kangaroo

CHAPTER 7

Maternity

Some of the laziest mothers in the animal kingdom are female cuckoos. After mating with several males and not choosing any particular one as her permanent companion, the female cuckoo goes off on her own searching for other birds to raise her young. When she finds a nest suitable for her purpose, she waits patiently until the owners are away, occupies the nest and lays her egg there. She needs to take two precautions so that the rightful owners of the nest do not realise anything is amiss. First, the egg must be the same size as those already in the nest and secondly the number in the nest must remain the same as before. But the cuckoo knows very well which eggs are similar to her own and there is no danger that she will make a mistake. If there are too many eggs, she just eats the extra ones and substitutes her own, so that the number is correct when the mother returns to count her eggs. A female cuckoo lays up to twenty eggs in different nests but never more than one in each. The small cuckoo is so greedy that its adopted parents cannot raise two young ones. Baby cuckoos grow big and fast and soon find themselves squeezed so tight that they push their adopted brothers out of the nest.

One bird which gets anxious about its eggs is the guilemot – a species of penguin which lives in Northern Europe. When it returns from a flight, it never makes a mistake about where it has left its only egg and lands at the exact spot, recognising the place even if the egg has been stolen. When this happens, the guillemot will pause for a few minutes' thought and then leave in search of the egg. It recognises it without any possibility of error by the colour and design and rolls it delicately back to its original position. The task is not easy because being pear-shaped, the egg's centre of gravity is displaced and it cannot achieve a direct line but goes round and round in small circles. When the chick is old enough, it is the task of one parent to teach it to swim and to fly which it does with a not particularly gentle method. It carries its chick to the edge of a slope and pushes it off balance so the small bird falls into the sea and learns to swim instantly by instinct. The time it does not want to swim it will try to open its wings and learns to fly in this way.

Swallows are not very tender either when they teach their young to fly. Certain species of swallows have babies twice a year and therefore must bring up their young as quickly as possible to make room for the new eggs. A tender and affectionate mother in the first instance the swallow drastically changes her method when she decides the time has come to wean her young. She suddenly stops feeding them and leaves them until their hunger grows, then brings some food to the nest in her beak and hovers a short distance away. The starving young are then forced to come out of their nest and can only satisfy their hunger when they have managed to fly out of their nest on their own to the mother.

The honeyguide, that strange bird, which makes contracts with the natives to get its beeswax, lays its eggs like the cuckoo in other birds' nests. But instead of waiting until the owners of the nest are away, the husband and wife induce them by deception to fly away from their nest just at the moment when they are laying their own eggs in the nest. The young are even larger than small cuckoos: they are born with a pair of sharp prickles on the point of their beaks and immediately kill their adopted brothers. After a fortnight, the young honeyguide loses its weapon, which it no longer needs, because it is now the only chick and devours all the food that its adopted parents can manage to find it: if it turns out that it has been born in a nest which is too small for it, the nest owners are obliged to enlarge it to make room for the bird.

Certain penguins, on the other hand, have the horrible habit of stealing eggs from other penguins, not to hatch them but to eat them. If the couple live together the male and female take turns to hatch the egg and never abandon it; if by chance, one of them becomes widowed and has to leave the egg, it places it between its legs and hops about with great difficulty.

The animal with the most maternal behaviour is the manatee, an acquatic mammal from the Rio region of the Amazon. It is about 3–4 metres long and in order to suckle its young, the mother raises it out of the water and presses it to her with her fins.

That delightful Australian marsupial, the koala bear, carries its young in transit one by one on its back. When one of them behaves badly, the mother slaps it on the nose just like any human mother.

The female sand pigeon lives in South West Africa and has a strange method of giving her young water to drink. She submerges herself in a puddle of water and returns to her nest immediately so that the young ones can drink the drops of water off her feathers.

Maternity can bring about miracles with certain animals. The python, for example, rolls up on its eggs, and manages to produce enough heat to hatch them. The green lizard cannot do this but contents itself with finding a warm, damp place where it deposits its eggs and then totally neglects them. The scrub turkey which lives in Australia and New Guinea builds itself a perfect incubator which takes away the chore of having to hatch the eggs. It covers them with enormous amounts of fungi and rotting plants which produce heat as they decompose.

Other fowls from the Celebes Islands, make their task even less arduous by utilising the sand around the edges of thermal streams, while certain birds from the Bismarck Archipelago bury their eggs right under the warm larva. It seems impossible that these discoveries could not be the fruit of rational thought: instinct, in fact, at least in warm-blooded animals, imposes on them a need to hatch their eggs but all these animals, perhaps motivated by laziness or boredom, have managed to discover that constant heat is equivalent to that of the body and obtains the same results as sitting on the eggs and is less trouble.

In Equatorial Africa there are birds which weave wool and bind it with leaves and pieces of bark to construct beautiful little basket-like nests; other more able birds make them into cup or bottle-shapes and hang them on branches over rivers or lakes so they are almost out of danger.

Another excellent mother is the kangaroo. Even today, this strange animal has not unveiled all its secrets. The first mystery is its name. When Captain Cook's sailors landed in Australia and saw this strange animal, they asked the natives what it was. The natives held up their hands in incomprehension and said 'Kan-ga-roo', meaning 'We do not know'. This marsupial is two-and-a-half centimetres long when it is born and is as transparent as an earthworm. It grows to the stature of a fully-grown man and reaches the respectable weight of 90 kilogrammes. When the little kangaroo is born, the only developed parts are its small hands which it needs immediately to clutch to its mother's fur and climb up into her pouch.

The small kangaroo attaches itself firmly to a milk gland but because of its size, it is not yet strong enough to suckle and would die of hunger if nature had not furnished the mother with special muscles with which she pushes milk into the baby kangaroo's mouth. How the little kangaroo manages to breathe during suckling has remained a mystery for years until naturalists discovered that when the baby kangaroo suckles it has an appendix on its larynx joined to the back part of its nostrils, so that air can pass directly into its lungs. At 4 months the kangaroo is weaned and covered with hair. It leaps out of the pouch on to the ground to eat grass with its mother but at the first sign of danger, it takes refuge in her pouch.

Another extremely maternal animal, in spite of its fierce aspect, is the eagle. The male is also an affectionate and solicitous father, although the baby eaglets do not give their parents much to do. After the first week of life, they already need 3 kilogrammes of food a day and in two-and-a-half months reach the same massive proportions as their parents and are able to fly. They gulp down meat, bones, feathers and skin in order to ingest everything they need. At the beginning, the mother snatches shreds of meat which she swallows and regurgitates into the mouths of the eaglets. Finally, she teaches her young to tear small victims into pieces with their beaks which they soon learn to do on their own. Since eaglets are generally born in pairs, one will grow stronger and more vigorous than the other. If then, for some reason, the two brothers are forced to starve for too long, the cruel law of the survival of the fittest brings tragedy: the sturdiest eaglet tears the other into pieces and eats him.

On the great day of their first flight, the parents push the eaglets into an abyss and they fall down into the void. Frantically, they beat their wings but the mother is always there ready to catch them on her back, if they cannot do it. By the time the first snow of the year falls, the eaglet is able to defend itself, fly perfectly and go hunting with its parents.

When rabbits are expecting their young, they prepare quilts made with their own fur and woven with blades of grass. The cover has a double function because, while it protects the young from the cold, it is also a perfect camouflage and protects them from danger as well.

The young opossum, which is a marsupial, is as small as a bee when it is born and weighs 2 grammes. It therefore needs a lot of protection but like the kangaroo, it is able to climb straight on to its mother where it finds all the protection it needs. When it has been weaned, the mother carries it around with her on her back. The numerous young lean their chin against her dorsal spine and cling tightly to her fur. Sometimes the mother arches her long tail round them in such a way that the little ones can attach their tails too, developing the prehensility which is so useful when they become adults.

When the female bat is near childbirth she hangs by her four feet and her head pointing downwards, with her wings spread out and her body forming a cradle for the newborn bat. Until it is weaned, the young bat goes around gripping on to its mother's chest with its teeth.

The female gorilla, which closely resembles humans in its habits, builds a proper cot with branches and covers it with leaves, while the father builds a refuge in a strategic position so the young gorilla will be constantly under their eyes where they can protect him from danger.

The polar bear makes a large bedroom for his offspring at the end of a gallery excavated from the snow, where just like eskimos in their igloos, the young bears are protected from the glacial winds.

The coyote which, as we know, willingly eats carrion crow abandoned by other predators, reveals her taste for the second-hand even in maternity but puts much care into raising her young. Instead of preparing a suitable den for her tastes and needs, she occupies one that has been abandoned by a badger or a marmot, and puts it into order enlarging it, cleaning it scrupulously and providing it with a rudimentary system of air conditioning. Nearly all mothers have a sublime respect for their children's hygiene and also clean surroundings. It is difficult to find an untidy den.

A difficult and risky task for the mothers of many young is that of moving. The mother bear which has to transport one young, but rather cumbersome cub, will take its whole head extremely delicately in her mouth without harming it.

There has long been a controversy over whether young animals learn by instinct or whether they are taught. The cat and mouse situation is one example. Do kittens run after mice by instinct or because their mothers have taught them to? Some scientists maintain that mother cats teach their young to chase mice and that they even pull their kitten's ears if they are too slow in learning. On the other hand, there are many domesticated cats which are taken from their mothers before having had the chance to come across mice. Kittens and mice raised together can be very friendly towards one another.

The otter, instead, uses a method which is also fashionable among humans. It suddenly takes the lifebelt from its young when they are learning to swim. The parent will swim in the river with its baby on its back, then dive downwards leaving the young otter to manage on its own. It knows it will not drown and is there ready to save it if anything goes wrong.

The mother flying squirrel has to throw her young from the tree to teach them to glide: an absolute necessity for this squirrel which is constantly threatened by the weasel. The weasel is one of the most ferocious and bloodthirsty creatures that exists, but a mother squirrel defending her young, will bite and scratch its head so much that it will run away.

All faculties are sharpened with animal mothers when the life of their young are in danger. Even though she is abandoned by her young at the earliest opportunity, while they are under her protection, they are sacred and woe betide anyone that touches them. Given half the chance, mothers can become extremely ferocious. We just need to think of the lioness, the tiger or the bear who are the most classic examples of this. Smaller and more defenceless animals use all their resources, courage and cunning.

The naturalist Alan Devoe tells how he once saw a mother marmot which, while a dog was digging furiously at her den, heaped up earth at the same rapid speed as the dog was digging. As the barricade was destroyed the marmot built another in a few seconds. Then another and then another, giving up her gallery little by little after an arduous struggle. He thought she would be the first to collapse with exhaustion but it was the dog who gave up and went away defeated.

Among birds, crows look after their young the longest and are excellent parents although Germans have a word for people they consider unnatural parents, 'rabeneltern' which means 'crow parents'. Young crows are always protected against temperature changes, and their nest is sufficiently padded against the cold so that all you can see is their beaks spouting over the top.

All mothers have their own ways for their young to recognise them, at least among species who do not recognise their mothers spontaneously like the geese we have seen. Some female birds even have a password for entering the nest.

The lioness makes her lion cubs recognise her, or calls them into order, by letting out a menacing rumble which has an instant effect. One of the most ferocious animals, the ork, is also one of the most solicitous and affectionate mothers. When her offspring is born it is already quite large and well developed and the mother pushes it to the surface for an immediate mouthful of air. Like dolphins, the ork is a mammal and suckles her young, but nature has endowed her with a sac in which mammary glands are embedded so her young can suckle without swallowing water. The family instinct is highly developed as is that of the whole shoals. If a female or young one is wounded, other females help it by pushing it out of danger. This sense of solidarity, which we have seen with elephants, seems more emphasised among the huge, more cumbersome animals, which, although conscious of their dimension which can at times be useful, is also a nuisance to them in times of danger.

In maternity, as in all their aspects, monkeys are the most interesting animals for us because they resemble man so closely. The chimpanzee can be domesticated and is a mother who is not only affectionate but very proud of her young.

One of the most famous chimpanzees in the world was Boo-Boo, who gave birth to Jubilee, the first chimp to be born at London Zoo. At the time of her birth 40 years ago, photos of the little chimp filled the English newspapers and almost outnumbered the pictures of Winston Churchill. At her birth, Jubilee received thousands of gifts from all over England which were more suited to human babies but which illustrated the English love and affection for animals.

Boo-Boo was very proud of her daughter, but also apprehensive and continually tried to ensure she did not run into any danger or hurt herself while climbing up the netting of her cage. Through an excess of maternal love, Boo-Boo did not have the slightest idea what was good or bad for an ape only a few months old, so to please her, she let her take and eat anything visitors offered her, ruining her basic diet of peeled grapes and orange squash which is the only food a young chimp is supposed to eat during its weaning stage.

Boo-Boo had such a great affection for her keeper that sometimes she would involve the small ape in her tricks to get his attention. If he went away, Boo-Boo pushed Jubilee to the ground and squashed her face against the soil until her shouts made the keeper turn round in his tracks. Before Jubilee was born, Boo-Boo had been a star turn in the zoo's daily events, but like many great actresses she abandoned the stage to become a good mother. With the strong affection she showed for her daughter, she was decidedly superior to the other chimps.

Another element was that Jubilee was the only child of Boo-Boo's one and only great love. Many vain attempts had previously been made to get Boo-Boo to mate, but she always rejected the robust young chimpanzees that were introduced to her and had been brought from far away. Then one day, quite unexpectedly, she got to know a small, fat and rather old chimpanzee with an enormous paunch and fell hopelessly in love with him. From this great love Jubilee was born.

One cannot talk about maternity in animals without mentioning the animal that has portrayed it for so many centuries, although it is now unfashionable, and more rational and less poetical explanations have been put forward. It is of course, the stork. It is becoming more and more difficult to believe this animal ever existed because it is disappearing so fast, even from zoos. The next generation will probably not even notice the loss because storks will have meant nothing to them, but people born in the first half of this century, will have a vague feeling that they have lost a dear friend.

Behind the legend that storks carry children into the world, lies the old belief that if a stork settled authoritatively on the roof of a house, it embodied the soul of an ancestor of the people living in that house, and it follows the birth of every new descendant with great interest. The maternal behaviour of the stork naturally has to be perfect so that the legend can be attributed to it. Its nest is a masterpiece. It is not just a refuge for one season but a stable abode which is enriched every year with new additions until it grows to a height of 2 metres. It is made of twigs and small branches which are woven and constructed on a solid base to prevent it from being blown away in the wind. A long time ago, storks used to build their nests on trees, but suddenly no one knows why they decided to bind their destiny to man and began choosing rooftops for their habitations. In his turn, man has always protected and welcomed storks with open arms, convinced that they bring good luck. A well-known and popular legend in Denmark says a stork's nest protects the house it is built on from thunderbolts and the owner of that house will become rich and live a long life.

Nothing disturbs a stork when it is hatching its eggs. Come rain, sun and wind the stork remains stationary sitting patiently through until the evening when it begins to scrutinise the sky to watch her companion arrive, and take his turn on the nest guarding the eggs. The two storks greet each other with the same ceremony which is repeated fifty times a day each time they meet. Whichever stork is on the nest, gets up, points its beak towards the other and clacks its jaws together. This same ceremony is taught to the young when they are scarcely old enough to learn it. When the parents arrive at the nest, the young storks rise up in a polite, educated manner and clack their beaks together.

For some mysterious reason, storks are fast becoming extinct. People want to save them but do not know how. Perhaps they are just coming to the end of their era, like so many legends do.

WORK·SPORT·PLAY

CHAPTER 8

Work, Sport and Play

Man is a born exploiter and will never miss an opportunity to make someone else work for him, especially if he does not have to pay. Leaving aside the commonest cases of horses pulling carriages or oxen ploughing fields, we will look at some of the more interesting examples.

Until a few years ago, it was not unusual to see flocks of ducks on rivers in China pulling their master to market while he sat tranquilly in a boat which hundreds of ducks hauled against the current. But the animal which has always been made to work the hardest, because of its intelligence and docility and its continual contact with man is the dog.

A cruel habit, fashionable in the nineteenth century in France and also, surprisingly, in dog-loving England consisted of making the dog prepare the family's meal by turning the meat on a roasting spit. The dog was shut in a revolving cage like a windmill wheel which was hung from the ceiling and attached to the spit by means of pulleys. The poor beast was made to run round uninterruptedly for 2–3 hours on end and turn the meat until it was cooked.

Sledge dogs must surely be the ones who undertake the hardest and most backbreaking work. Until 30 years ago, they were the only means of travelling in the five million square miles of North America which stretches from the 60° parallel up to 800 kilometres from the North Pole. And today, it is still the only means of transport in a large part of the region.

There are three types of sledge dogs: the Malemut of Western Alaska, the Siberian dogs used by the Russians when they occupied Alaska, and the pure-blooded original race found in Northern Canada.

A typical example of this dog is about 60 centimetres tall and 1 metre 12 centimetres long from the point of its nose to the tip of its tail. It weighs between 25 and 54 kilogrammes. The female is smaller and lighter. The dogs have broad, muscular chests with strongly built necks and solid paws. The fur is a work of art in its adaptation to the climate: it is 10–15 centimetres long and beneath is another layer of oily wool about 5–7 centimetres thick. Thus protected the dog can bear extremes of cold up to minus 45°C without any need of shelter.

The Esquimaux dog does not bark but lets out a howl which can easily be confused with its bitter enemy, the wolf. The unbelievable resistance of this race allows the female to pull very heavy loads right up to the day she gives birth. About seven or eight pups are born, usually in a small igloo kennel built by the owner. Training begins at around 8 months when the owner puts one or two of them in a relay. The older dogs are not the kindliest of instructors. They rebuke and bite the new conscripts until they know their place and their job.

When the females are on heat, they try to conquer the strongest and the quickest dog. In the case of these dogs there is no hierarchy to respect which is usually rigid with other animals. The only supremacy respected is that of the leader of the pack during work. These dogs are famous for being ferocious and cruel but this is mostly unfounded. Ferocity is due only to the perpetual appetite of these poor beasts; the cold is very acute and the dogs work extremely hard, a team of twelve to fifteen dogs pulling about 400 kilogrammes, and food is scarce.

Work takes place in the worst of conditions. The team leader is a real slave-driver, paying great attention to catching out the laziest. Sometimes the dogs' muzzles become congealed with the icy winds and their lungs freeze up with the cold and the excessive effort, often causing fatal haemorrhages. If the snow is slippery, small pellets of ice form between their claws which can lame or cripple them. And a lame husky might as well be a dead one – eskimos do not have enough food to squander on useless animals. Even so, these dogs continue to serve them faithfully and selflessly instead of emigrating to another place where life could be easier.

I once knew a sledge dog that was good, sweet and affectionate unless anyone touched her bread which she was guarding jealously. Although she was well fed, she was convinced through her inherited fear of hunger, that it would be stolen. She had been brought from the North, perhaps by tourists who had been moved at the difficult life she lived there. In Italy, she first lived on a large estate near Turin where big hunts took place. But she was not a hunting dog and finished up in a villa in the hills among a lot of dogs of different species and a garden full of flowers. She was the mildest of all the dogs there and never quarrelled, not even over a loaf of bread. Once or twice she slaughtered some chickens but she soon learned that the laws of the extreme North did not go down well in Turin households. I do not know at what age she was taken from the North but she lived in that house for 12 years without ever showing signs of intolerance. When it snowed she was happy and rolled about in it to the amazement of the other dogs; but in the summer in spite of her double fur coat, she was just as happy to bask in the sun.

A similar worthy job is done by those other workers, avalanche dogs. They are German sheepdogs whose particular gifts lie in being able to find bodies buried under the snow. Avalanche dogs are different from the famous Saint

Bernard which can actually see men who are lost in the snow and can smell the presence of a man buried under the snow, and are infallible provided they are called out in time. These dogs were 'discovered' by the Swiss, Ferdinand Schmutz during the Second World War.

Schmutz had always loved dogs and since he was a child often helped a police friend and pretended to be a burglar followed by a police dog. Just before the war, Schmutz read a story in the newspaper about Moritz, a dog who had saved the life of a skier buried by an avalanche. He made some enquiries and discovered that Moritz was an untaught mongrel which had, by chance, been with his master at the place of the calamity. Of the fifteen skiers buried by snow the rescue team had pulled out fourteen, but the fifteenth remained hidden. All of a sudden, the dog began scratching at the snow and barking, and refused to obey his master when he was told to sit still. Finally, the helpers decided to dig where the dog was scratching and there found the last and fifteenth skier.

Schmutz tried to repeat the experiment with Moritz by placing volunteer skiers in various spots and covering them with snow. But the dog ignored them completely, wagging his tail happily as if he knew it was a game and not for real. The experiment finished there but Schmutz did not let go of the idea that by continuous training he could obtain a squad of excellent avalanche dogs. He was proved right in the Second World War, when he was allotted five Red Cross dogs, which had already been taught to search and mark the spot where the wounded were. Schmutz taught them to do this when avalanches happened and so great was his success that one month later he was given another fifty dogs and then another fifty each year. The dogs proved to be extremely valuable during the war and saved many lives. After the war, they were sold for a small sum to the men they had worked with and they were reorganised privately by alpine clubs, in order not to waste Schmutz's teaching.

The dogs have never failed but men have often failed them by not trusting them. The only slight defect these wonderful dogs have is that they cannot distinguish between the smell of a man and the smell of other animals.

Other more well-known workers are police dogs. The best breed for this task is, as usual, the German sheepdog, which merits the status of being called the king of dogs. Bloodhounds, with their long ears and sad, wrinkled faces are born seekers whether they are searching for a beetle or a man, and can be relied upon absolutely infallibly. Delinquents fear them not because they are fierce – they are docile and affectionate – but because once they are recognised by these dogs they know they can never escape. But German sheepdogs are completely different. If properly instructed, they are fierce enough to attack a man and hold him prisoner until they are called off by their master.

People who have seen exhibitions of police dogs with their instructors and all the apparatus they haul out for demonstrations cannot possibly ignore their incredible gifts of intelligence, strength and courage.

Dox, an Italian dog, was the most intelligent, strongest and bravest dog of all. He won all the international competitions, and even beat the great Rex of Scotland Yard, who accomplished almost 220 police operations and retrieved dozens of people who were wounded. Dox must be one of the only dogs to ever receive a fixed salary. In 1960, when he was fourteen, he earned 35,000 lire a month – very little when you look at his incredible list of successes. Rome's Chief of Police declared that Dox was one of the best men in the force. He belonged to a Sergeant Maimone who had bought him as a 2-month-old puppy and taught him himself, perhaps sensing his enormous capabilities. Dox quickly showed that not only was he an excellent tracker dog but also extremely intelligent and an able investigator.

Once Maimone fell into an ambush set for him by the bandit, Giuliano and was left dying in a mountain cave with four bullets in his stomach and two in his shoulder. Dox was still quite young and fresh from training, and 'knew' he should follow the bandit but 'sensed' there was something more urgent to do – to save his master. He went to fetch help and Maimone's life was saved.

One night a thief broke into a jeweller's shop in Rome. The theft was discovered by the nightwatchman but after a brief struggle the thief escaped. Dox was brought in and immediately picked up the thief's scent from the night-watchman's jacket, and began to follow his trail. He led the policemen to a cellar in another quarter of Rome where they found a man fast asleep. The man had been convicted before and managed to convince the police he had nothing to do with the jewel robbery. Dox was scolded for his blunder, but still sure of his fact, he barked at his master, set off again and returned to the jeweller's shop where he picked up a button at the back of the shop, which he placed in his master's hand. Perceiving the dog's certainty Maimone decided to trust him. Dox barked again and led them back to the suspect's cellar where he was sleeping peacefully, sure he had shaken them off.

But the implacable dog headed towards the cupboard, opened it and pulled out a raincoat and pointed with his nose to where the broken cotton showed a button was missing. It was, without the shadow of a doubt, the missing button which had been found in the jewellers. It was perhaps after this episode that the police learned to trust implicitly in their dogs and never doubt their 'word'.

Guide dogs for the blind, too, earn their living in a sense. Although they do not pay taxes they have absolute respon-sibility for a life that is entrusted to their safekeeping. These dogs never enjoy themselves and do not even have the small reward or excitement of being on someone's tracks or the joy of finally finding the sought-after object. All they have is their consciousness of the job they do, and sometimes, one hopes, the affection and gratitude of those who owe their independence to them.

Let us pass on to happier things and stop talking of animals working for us and look at those which amuse us instead. Fortunately, animals do not imitate man only at work but also at play, in games and in sport. If the essence of man is game, animals, too, are not adverse to this, not only when they are young but many of them continue enjoying themselves in play all their lives.

The great English naturalist, W. H. Hudson, tells how he was once sleeping in the Argentine Pampas when he was awoken by a puma's cry. By the light of the moon, he saw four huge pumas come up to him. As he lay there motionless and terrified for some fear-filled minutes, in which he believed his end had come, he realised that the large cats, far from attacking him, were playing and enjoying themselves on their own account, accepting him as a spectator. They were like four grown kittens, jumping, running and skipping right over his body without even glancing at him. When their games were over, the pumas went off without molesting him at all.

All the most highly evolved animals play. Even the terrible grey bear, one of the fiercest animals that exists, amuses a lot of people by sliding down snow-covered slopes just like a small boy on a toboggan. They do it over and over again, climbing wearily up the slope time after time. All bears love rolling: an American bear cub once found an open-ended barrel, got inside and wriggled around until it turned over and he rolled down the hill.

The larger animals are, the more their games resemble man's. A herd of elephants was once seen kicking a rudimentary ball of earth around in a game which seemed very like football; but the main difference lay in the size of the ball which was half a metre in diameter and also in the rule which permitted the use of the trunk but did not comment on the lack of striped football shirts.

The ugly, clumsy hippopotamus has his own games. Some years ago in Amsterdam Zoo, a hippo discovered a game to play on its own. A large leaf was placed on the surface of the water where it floated and then the hippo would swim under the leaf, blow gently through his nostrils and blow the leaf up into the air. He would do this for hours on end with an expression of absolute ecstasy on his face.

Small American badgers get close to what is taught in schools today as practical skills. They search for pieces of rough wood and amuse themselves, with no particular end in view, by polishing them.

The gopher, a rodent who lives in the American prairies plays our game of puss in the corner, each one seeking to occupy the other's den and playing hide and seek while he is away. It is interesting to see the cunning applied in this game in attempting to place obstacles in the other's way.

Roe bucks play hide and seek with such speed and dexterity that practising the game is useful to them in later life and quite a few of them owe their lives to it during some pursuit.

The step from games to sport is a short one when they are not mixed together, and in the case of animals, rules are very strict and fair play is an absolute necessity. Porcupines fight frequently and willingly but without ever pricking themselves or each other. However ruthless the fight may be, lashing out with their spiny tails is forbidden and no porcupine would ever dream of contravening that rule.

Badgers box, too, but the best boxer of all is the kangaroo. Anyone seeing it fight would think it had had a lengthy training from a famous show-boxer. Boxing comes instinctively to kangaroos and they will always do it gladly and sometimes against human beings.

Crows are some of the most playful creatures existing and here there is a similarity with man. Their favourite recreation is chasing and they will often go to great lengths of cunning to procure a playmate. The crow that wants to play goes up to one of his laziest companions and places a fresh worm at his feet as if he were giving him a present. But when the other crow picks the gift up, it is immediately snatched from his beak and the first crow flies away with it. Full of indignation, the lazy crow follows and the original aim is fulfilled – the game has begun.

Acrobatics and balancing games are also much played by crows. They do exercises by hanging on by one claw to the smaller branches of trees swinging round and round and flapping their wings. Then they also dare their companions to imitate them. The spirit of imitation among crows is very great and pushes them into doing all sorts of things so as not to appear inferior to other crows.

Naturally, once man was aware of the sporting traits of animals, he lost no time in turning them to his own advantage and organising spectacles such as circuses with animals as the chief protagonists.

It follows the principle of the absurd which is what amuses the public: the slower an animal is the more he is made to run, the clumsier he is the more skilful things he is made to do. Every year, the world snail championships are held in Brighton. In the last few years, one of the best records was held by Collie, a mother of sixteen, who managed to complete the 60 centimetre race in just 4 minutes.

As there is a snail race, so naturally there is a tortoise race. One takes place every year at Lillington in North Carolina, and is closely followed throughout the whole state. Some time ago, even Alabama's governor, George Wallace, put his small tortoise, George, in for the race, which it won covering the dizzy distance of 4·57 metres in exactly 57 seconds. But the most important tortoise race is the one that takes place every year at Poca City, U.S.A. It is called the Terrapin Derby and covers a circular track of 22 metres. The competition has been going on for nearly a century now and until 1948 the record was held by Bill who covered the distance in 1 minute, 28·02 seconds.

In Germany, Susie, the piglet has become very popular on television. She spends an hour each day doing the high jump and after every exhibition like every good German, she revives herself with a large tankard of beer.

The natural tendency of crickets to fight has been exploited in Thailand where it is the object of considerable betting. The two crickets are enclosed in a glass box and prodded with small sticks.

It is too well known to dwell on lengthily here but like dog-racing, cockfighting is very popular in England. While there may be a spirit of competition among dogs, cockfighting cannot be considered a sport, but is a cruel and bloodthirsty spectacle. I will not even mention bullfights as I consider them to be well below the basest human level.

Since every country has its share of sporting animals, we must not forget Turkey where fighting camels are bred. This type of fight is no more bloodthirsty than our boxing and there is no danger that either of the two contestants will lose their lives. In fact, the national championships take place every year with very high wagers and champions sometimes remain at the top for several consecutive years.

The strangest sport an animal has ever done must be parachuting. There is a German sheepdog, who does this enthusiastically. Called Tasso, he belongs to Robert Tagwerker, who takes him with him to all the aeronautic shows and jumps out with him at 1,200 metres.

The most widespread sport among animals whether through natural tendencies or after being taught, is underwater chase. The dipper drags all his food from the water and is equipped effectively as the perfect frogman. There is a gland above his tail which secretes fat so that when he dives the bird smears himself all over with this grease which makes him almost completely waterproof as he dives head first into the water. When he goes for an underwater walk, he enlarges his wings to keep him on the bottom. His eyes are protected by two membranes embellished with white feathers. When he captures his prey, he shoots up to the surface of the water. Naturally, the dipper always builds his nest close to the water so it can teach its young this sport at the earliest opportunity since it will be meat and drink to them in the future.

You often see dogs swimming but to see a dog completely equipped as a frogman is still a novelty. An underwater diver has taught his terrier to dive perfectly so that it is now an infallible assistant to him underwater. The dog wears a mask, an oxygen supply on its back and small rubber flippers so it does not injure itself on the rocks. It seems certain that the best divers are insects although it is difficult to substantiate this.

Winter sports are difficult for animals. As far as we know there are no animal skiers, but a horse in the U.S.A. has been taught to walk on snow with snowshoes and it seems quite happy to do so.

Speedy, an agreeable German basset hound I know, takes it in good heart to go tobogganing, as long as he is guided by someone he knows well and is wearing a woollen beret on his head.

BVILDERS

CHAPTER 9

Builders

The profession which is most practised in the animal kingdom is building. Builders are equally distributed among the inhabitants of air, land and water and their work can, at times, be classed as true masterpieces of technique and appear to be based on a perfect knowledge and application of the law of physics and geometry.

Beginning with the smallest animals, we find that various species of ants have architectural gifts. Aztec ants, for example, from Southern Central America, have invented cardboard architecture. To build their nests, they finely grind down soft wood from dead trees and knead it with saliva, obtaining a material identical to cardboard.

The best builders are termites whose constructions are incomparable examples of functionalism and perfect from every point of view. We will examine some of these builders and their peculiarities more closely. The nests of African termites can grow to a height of 8 metres and a circumference of 15 metres. The longest side always points in an east-west direction and the structure is covered with cement which is several decimetres thick.

But what strikes one most is the interior. Air ducts are farsightedly placed in certain cells which are kept at a constant temperature for the young – air conditioned nurseries perhaps? The queen's apartment is made up of a large number of cells clustered together which are larger than the normal ones and which have functional uses. One is built in a particularly damp spot and is adapted to the growing of microscopic fungi which constitute part of the termites' diet.

David Hancocks, an architect, has written a particularly interesting book on animal builders entitled *Master Builders of the Animal World*. He divides constructions into different types: building by subtraction, building by addition, underwater building and co-operative building. It is a method which has several benefits, not the least being that it allows the division into a few groups of animals which belong to the most diverse species and often have nothing in common but their building methods.

One of the creatures which is most useful to other creatures and to man is the woodpecker. Nature has given this bird a well-defined task, which is to destroy pernicious insects and it does this in the best possible way.

There are over 179 different types of woodpeckers and each species has been given particular organs to dislodge various insects. For example, the small downy American woodpecker clears maggots, grubs and caterpillars from the bark and crevices of trees, while the ant-eater woodpecker is very fond of ants. But the woodpecker does not interest us in its capacity as an insect exterminator so much as its other function which is a consequence of this: The woodpecker is an indefatigable builder of homes for the homeless. In fact, when it bores a hole in trees to ferret out insects, the holes it leaves constitute ready-made nests for other birds which take immediate possession. This does not matter to the woodpecker, because these holes are nothing like its own nest which is more complicated. The ability of the woodpecker to judge the strength of the wood in which it wants to build its own nest, is fantastic. It never miscalculates, not even by a millimetre – even if more than half the weight of the entire tree is weighing down upon the point it has attacked with its beak. The hole is always bored in such a way as not to risk the balance of the tree and therefore of the woodpecker itself. It is an extremely far sighted animal. To protect its nest from rain and wind, the woodpecker hollows out a gallery towards the top which constitutes the entrance, then it constructs a long, vertical cavity low down where its nest will be.

The woodpecker is even far-sighted towards its food. Fearful of not being able to find enough insects to feed off in the winter it makes enormous provisions of nuts and acorns, hollowing out a small hole for each one in the tree where its nest is situated. Once, 50,000 acorns were found in one gigantic pine tree.

When one speaks of animals with underground lairs, we immediately think of that ultimate excavator, the mole. The mole is a solitary and unsociable animal, except during its brief love-making period and it spends its entire life digging out galleries and hunting insects. The galleries are extremely complex and built on different levels according to the season of the year. In the summer when it is easier to find insects in the upper layers of the soil, the mole digs shallow galleries. In winter, however, galleries are built so deep that it is able to hunt below the frost level. There are some intermediate galleries which are used in all seasons and which become solid and resistant. But even they can crumble under heavy weights and the mole then has to undertake the difficult work of reconstruction. Generally, it digs a circular by-pass but at other times, especially when the earth is clayey, it repairs the roof, attaching pieces of earth to it and forming arches, after which it compresses the whole structure with its robust forelegs.

Moles sometimes dig open galleries when the earth is too unstable to support a roof. The famous mole fortresses have become legendary through the descriptions of many writers, but they are rare and difficult to find. According to those who have examined them carefully, these buildings cannot be compared to the constructions of beavers. A fortress can contain galleries, store-houses and hunting territories and, of course, a bedroom lined with dry grass and leaves. It has been discovered that fortresses are built chiefly in areas subject to flooding for defence reasons. But there is still a lot to discover about these ingenious builders.

Bees are just as able in the field of building. In Britain there are more than 250 species of bees and of all these only a few have a social life and build hives. Many are the so-called 'miner' bees and their hive is a particularly interesting building in which the female builds a vertical gallery, sometimes as long as a man's arm. On the bottom, she builds small recesses, sometimes covered with paper and furnished with a layer of honey and manure. On this bed of luxury she deposits the egg and then closes the cell with earth and builds another one immediately on top. The female bee builds about half a dozen cells like this all along the length of the gallery and each one containing an egg. When the work is completed, the bee returns to the surface and dies.

There are also potter bees which dig the earth at the bottom of the tunnel where they build tiny clay pots lined with honey and with droppings. The egg is deposited inside the pot and it is sealed up. Carpenter bees make their hives in the trunks of rotting trees, excavating a tunnel parallel to the veins of the trees, and in constructing cells for their eggs they use the sawdust they make during their excavations. Leaf-cutter ants prefer to use existing holes but they do not have any the less work because of it. They cut semi-circular portions from rose leaves which they roll into a cigar shape and then divided between the sealed up holes. Each cell contains an egg and when the hive is finished the mother dies. When the young bees are born they have to eat their way out of their nests.

Spiders

Among animals which build by addition, the king is the

spider. This repellent animal which is feared and hated more than mice and snakes, is a real master of ingenuity and reveals an amazing knowledge of the laws of physics in its constructions. If one thinks that there are more than forty thousand different kinds of spiders in the world, you can imagine the consequently enormous varieties of webs, each small masterpieces in their own right.

Let us look broadly at the structure of an orb web which is the commonest and the most perfect web which anyone can see in a garden. The thread of the web is formed by secretions from the spider's silk glands, known as the spinnerule – a control valve near the abdomen. Webs are spun by pairs of spiders and sometimes three couples. When a spider constructs its web, the points of the spinnerule approach each other so that the spurts of secretion unite into a single thread. The tension of a spider's silk is superior to steel and can be pulled for a fifth of its length before breaking. The threads you can see with the naked eye are very small ropes formed by weaving fine threads together. Certain threads have a diameter of 25 millionths of a millimetre.

The first strand of a web, the bridge line, is attached in an almost horizontal position. The head is attached to a grass or a twig and then the spider climbs up to another high point and stretches the thread across. When the thread is attached to something, the spider fixes the free end. Then it drops a vertical thread from one end, stretching another bridge line lower down than before. Then it drops a second vertical thread to the other end and forms a provisional structure.

Inside this framework, the spider pulls the strands taut and at the centre weaves a thick net called the hub. Around this it builds a first internal spiral on which it hangs while it builds, using a stickier material, the viscid thread for the external spiral with which it catches insects. The woven trap is ready. Now the spider needs a hiding place where it can await its prey. It takes a leaf, rolls it up and weaves a nest of silk inside. Then it stretches a telegraph thread from the centre of the web to its hiding place. The telegraph thread only has to shake and the spider knows its prey has fallen into the trap. When the insect struggles against one of the connecting cross threads which support the web, the thread springs like elastic and throws the victim into the net.

If the insect is relatively large, the spider hurries to add new threads and to pull and reinforce the old ones, raising his prey higher so it cannot escape. Spiders the size of peas have been seen trapping mice and even small snakes. Naturally, spiders come in a variety of shapes and sizes. The web of the Madagascan spiders can reach a size of 1·5 metres in diameter. The largest of all are the webs of the social spiders which work in co-operatives and build webs 10 metres long. There is also the Argyroneta spider which finishes off its web with a zig-zag decoration like a signature and this design varies from species to species, permitting identification.

Even though naturalists have long denied insects any knowledge of physics, many spiders use a counter-balance, generally a small stone, to maintain the tautness of the web. All the webs we have examined so far are cobweb traps, but there are also cobweb homes and these have two functions. Here we are talking of the larger, more regular webs which have a sort of silk bag in the middle which the spider uses as a place to live in and a nest in which to rear its young.

The weaving ant (oecophylla) is very common in the Tropics and lives in coffee plantations where it builds a nest using a technique similar to that of the spider by weaving a web between two leaves. Adult ants do not have silk glands but their larvae do and this does not go unused. The nest is built as follows: a squadron of worker ants with a great many jaws and legs between them, approach two leaves and unite them while another squadron of ants arrives bearing larvae. They place the larvae on the edge of the leaf, which secrete some adhesive substance each time. The ant and its living shuttle weaves a solid web between the two leaves which remain perfectly stuck together.

There are also builders among fish: the stickleback, for example, weaves aquatic grass into a ball to protect its egg. Certain species of frogs, even though rare, build themselves a rough copy of a nest. A bat builds a kind of curtain using the leaves of cut palms. The most well-known builder by addition, the beaver, is too often spoken of to dwell on here. Suffice it to say that there are two types of beavers; the lair beaver which can only excavate its lair and the lodge beaver which is capable of undertaking architectural miracles. In the United States, there is a dam on the Jefferson River built by beavers which is 640 metres long and 6 metres wide.

Swifts in Malaysia and Indochina produce a type of gelatinous saliva which hardens on contact with the air. It is used to build nests and dispenses with the need to search for building materials. Man has discovered that this substance is not only edible but also very tasty and the nests are therefore much sought after. This is the origin of the famous Birds Nest Soup which appear on all menus in Chinese restaurants.

One of the most ingenious builders among birds is the tailor bird, a melodious songbird, common in the gardens of India and China. It uses its long, sharp beak as a needle to sew two large leaves together as a basis for its nest. It pierces holes at the edge of the leaves and sews them together using vegetable fibre as a thread or silk from a cocoon or some cotton. Each point is separated and finished off with a knot on the outside of the leaf.

Without a doubt the most able builders are birds: nearly all of them build nests.

Builders exist among the most unexpected animals and where one would least expect to find them. For example, the common millipede builds a complete room in which it lays and keeps its eggs. It mixes saliva with fragments of faeces and earth shaping them into small pellets which, when joined together, form the basis of a circular wall. The eggs are placed in the middle and the millipede spends another day building the roof.

The strangest occurrence among reptiles, seeing that they all lay eggs, is that only alligators bother to build nests rather similar to birds' nests. Other animals often abandon their eggs to any danger. But the preoccupation with nests is much greater among amphibians which build rather skilful nests.

The grey African spider, for example, which lives in trees, secrets a mucus which the male beats with its front legs like egg whites until it has the consistency of uncooked meringue. Its nest is always built on trees on the river banks or over water, so that once the young are self-supporting they can make a hole in the bottom and jump into the water below.

Among mammals the most perfect nests are built by squirrels, especially the red European squirrel. It is not rare for this animal to use the empty nest of a crow or a magpie as the basis for its nest. It perfects it and then completes it with outer weavings of twigs, grass, mosses and skin. The height of modern refinement seems to be that the male and the female sleep in separate rooms and build another larger room for their young ones.

The most perfect structure in the mammal world is built by the dormouse. This sleepy little animal is so busy with its own comfort that it has a summer residence and a winter residence. The summer one is a masterpiece of weaving. It is a round nest, woven from long strands of grass and often suspended between two ears of corn, lined with vegetable fibre and clumps of pressed grass. In winter, the dormouse retires underground where it has an entire warehouse of provisions.

One gross error originating with apes is the belief that, because they are nearest to humans in behaviour and the most capable of imitating our various activities, they must imitate us in our architectural activities. But this is not so. Apes do not build, neither do they do any work. They content themselves with a pallet for the night which they change every evening, and which can be in the trees or on the ground.

There is an example which illustrates this clearly. Some years ago, an orang-utan escaped from its cage in London Zoo. It built something resembling a nest in a tree where it spent the night. The next morning it returned peacefully to its cage without any need of force or compulsion, and had its breakfast. Its demonstration was quite clear and from that moment on, all the apes in the Zoo were given materials to build nests and sleeping places with.

Octopuses build too, and their compulsive need to be between four walls can lead them to madness and sometimes even death if they are ever deprived of a refuge. If materials are at their disposal they build houses of stones, shells and pieces of rock. Anything will do as long as it serves as a refuge with one tiny exit to allow the owner of the house to come and go and to keep enemies and curious strangers at bay. But if the octopus comes across a hollow object in the sea with nothing inside and which could be used as a shelter, it will immediately adapt it as a house. Human skulls serve this purpose very well. The octopus is fiercely proud of its privacy and is therefore afraid to be without a refuge and if in captivity with no means of shelter or the materials to build one, it becomes one of the fiercest and most dangerous animals you can imagine.

The viscacha, an Argentinian rabbit, builds its warren with a perfect defence system. It builds up barriers in front of the entrance to the gallery using a bit of everything besides earth – for example, tufts of grass, various pebbles and other small objects which it finds. If its gallery should cave in and the inhabitants get buried and unable to get out, neighbouring rabbits will run and help immediately and also assist them with the rebuilding. But the neighbour's dwelling and one's own are absolutely sacred in the viscacha's world, even if it is being pursued by a dog, this rabbit will never enter another's warren. It will only consider this possibility if it is in imminent and certain danger of death.

Paper wasps can produce a paper-like substance by mixing wood cuttings with saliva and forming hexagonal cells. Working in co-operatives, they achieve buildings whose firmness is due more to their form than to the material used. These buildings also have to stand up to a whole season, in other words, the duration of a generation of wasps.

It is perhaps the hunter wasp known by the somewhat high-sounding name of *ammophila sphex* which should be placed in a supreme position for its use of the oddest building materials. This ferocious little animal paralyses a grub without killing it and then lays its eggs on top of it. It then covers them with pressed earth which it obtains by beating the earth repeatedly with a small stone which it holds between its jaws.

HIERARCHIES

Wolves

CHAPTER 10

Hierarchies

Animal hierarchies are often more inflexible than human ones and, at times, assume paradoxical forms. This happens chiefly in monarchical societies like those of bees or termites, where the queen is different in her physical structure. A queen termite can grow to the size of a sausage and also differs in her life cycle from the other termites. The most hierarchically structured societies are undoubtedly those of bees and ants. In bee societies, divisions within the beehive correspond to the division of work between bees belonging to different classes. The 20,000 to 40,000 bees in a hive excluding the queen, the virgin princesses and the males, belong to the unique worker class. This class is further divided, according to the jobs of the various workers. If one looks at the male bees – the drones – which are small in number in comparison with superior animals, one sees that they have no power. Their unique function is to fertilise the princesses, as indeed the unique function of the princesses is to be fertilised.

Guards are privileged workers and stand at the entrance to the hive. It is their job not to allow foreign bees to enter the hive. They let in the worker bees which go out to work and can recognise them by their smell (the antennae of the bee has 12,000 sense organs). A bee which tries to get into a hive that is not his own will be immediately recognised and killed. Other privileged workers are those which suckle and administer the queen bee with the famous royal jelly, which is the secretion from glands which only wet nurse bees have on their heads. The worker bees go out and collect nectar and pollen which they take to other workers who, with the glandular secretions, transform it into honey. This assembly chain ends with a third group of workers, endowed with special glands to transform honey into beeswax.

There are also workers adapted to humbler, more tiresome kinds of work: those who see to the ventilation of the hive by continually flapping their wings; those employed in cleaning the hive and those who build the new cells.

Observing such a perfectly structured society, we must naturally ask ourselves how order is maintained constantly and how each bee fulfils its task so calmly without rebelling or even wanting to aspire to a higher class. The answer is at once both simple and incredible: bees are destined for their different tasks by nature itself, according to their age. With the passing of time, their bodies undergo different transformations, developing new glands, while others disappear. Each bee, in its brief life cycle, will at some time, undertake all the work in a hive. Some scholars have shown this adaptability of bees through experiments. If the well-being of the hive demands it, the development of a bee can accelerate enormously.

The most interesting experiment was undertaken by the Russian scholar, L. I. Perepelova, who tried to take a queen, its larvae and its eggs from a hive to see whether the structure of the drones would crumble, if once deprived of the centre around which their life revolved.

And the incredible happened: after a few weeks of agitation and evident preoccupation among all the workers, some of them began laying eggs and were waited upon attentively by the wet-nurse bees. They laboriously laid six to eight eggs a day, compared with the 2,000 to 3,000 of the queen, but it was still a miracle because drones usually remain sterile all their lives and do not step out of line into a higher social class. The scholar concluded that evidently there was an inhibiting factor always present in the workers which prevented them from laying eggs, but which disappeared when the good of the community demanded it.

If hierarchies and development can be accelerated, can the opposite occur? Is it possible to adapt bees to functions they have already undertaken and rejuvenate them? Such an experiment was undertaken: the queen bee and her larvae were left with only the drones which had already passed through their wet-nurse stage and whose jelly glands had atrophied. There was no question of any choice: if the drones did not return to their former level of wet-nurse, all the larvae would die. But this was understood and even more miraculous is the fact that they did rejuvenate and their atrophied glands began to fill with royal jelly.

Still keeping bees in mind as far as insects are involved, let us examine a small animal which is not generally held in much esteem, and is often detested and feared – the mouse.

The mouse is essentially a social animal. His life is organised in groups which occupy sheltered areas and is subordinated to a strict hierarchy which establishes itself through ritual fighting.

Throughout time, some aggressive gestures, designed to impose supremacy, have been transformed into signs, which have the same effect, in as much as the other mouse will respond with a corresponding sign of submission. In this way, much bloodshed is avoided, providing the mouse, which is the object of the dominant mouse's attentions, is disposed towards it. In this case the mice revert to the old system of fighting and the victory is won, not by the most arrogant or bullying mouse, but the physically strongest.

Mouse society is a closed one with a tendency to consanguinity. In plain words, if the society depended upon the males, the group of mice would remain uniform and matings would only happen within the group, so that practically all the offspring would come from the same father, since the dominant male has a right to breed with all the females in the group.

But fortunately things happen differently and the capricious females, instinctively knowing that they would have little choice in their marital affairs within the group, develop strong sexual preferences for males of other groups, to the point that even if they are already fertilised by a male of their own group, they will endure a pregnancy blockade until they meet a male from another group. Their strategy is dictated not by cunning but by nature in order to obtain the genetic exchange which is a basic necessity for the life of mice.

Hens, generally considered rather simple animals, also have rigid hierarchies, which are determined not by brute force alone but by energy, audacity and confidence. Hierarchies among chickens tend to degenerate into dictatorships as with men, and inspire hens with a holy terror of their superiors, while they recognise inferiors instantly on whom they vent their anger. The pecking order is sacrosanct and no hen dares dispute it.

With animals, as with men, the hierarchical scale unfailingly leads to snobbism. It was Konrad Lorenz who referred to an episode which illustrates this. A male magpie was enamoured with a female of a much lower social scale than his. Their voices rose in haste and unison, and after a few days, the whole colony knew they had to respect the male magpie's chosen wife, even though she was a mere nothing and had formerly been treated badly by the other magpies. But, like many people, the female bird became swollen-headed and knew she could now do what she wanted without fear of being rebuked. She began abusing her social position. This young magpie, as Lorenz commented, completely lacked any of the noble tolerance that magpies of a higher class show towards their inferiors. She never let an opportunity pass to wreak revenge on those who had previously despised her. In brief, she was behaving in a vulgar fashion.

Jellyfish, too, at times have sketchy hierarchies, or at least a sub-division of tasks: the dwarf species (nanomia) groups its individuals into enormous bunches: some have the duty of finding food, others of absorbing it, others providing the necessary force to defend an entire colony and finally there are those who are charged with laying the eggs.

Dogs rarely live in groups. When they do, like sledge dogs, there is always a head who leads and urges the other dogs on. He is perfectly conscious of his authority and very proud of it, up to the point that if the owner makes him change places, he will refuse to work, and rebels and pines away. In fact, he goes on strike until the owner puts him back into his proper place.

Hierarchies are particularly well developed among birds where there is a vertical hierarchy in which the most important individual dominates all the others. The second most important individual dominates all but one, the third all but two and so on, right through to the last bird which is dominated by every bird and has no rights over any of them. Sexual hierarchy is articulated in the same way, too. In a group of capercaillies, for example, the first one will accomplish 75 per cent of the fertilisations, the second only 22 per cent and the remaining males 3 per cent. The subordinated males have little to do and are entrusted with the task of protecting the females from the possible advances of males from other groups. 'Look but don't touch' is the attitude and, in fact, just what eunuch guards had to do in the harems in times of antiquity. In this case, the hierarchy is very stable and with nearly all the animals who have marriage contracts, the wife acquires the same social class as her husband.

But hierarchies are not always vertical and can be more complex. In bovines, for example, there is a triangular

hierarchy. Individual A dominates individual B who dominates individual C who dominates individual A. Therefore,
the possibility of dispute exists and every so often the social
positions are placed under discussion. This, of course, is the
type of hierarchy which is the least likely to degenerate into
dictatorship, but triangular hierarchies are often combined
with vertical ones and the result is that, in general, individual A dominates all the others.

Before summer pasture in the mountains, cows fight
among themselves to decide who will lead the expedition.
The fight takes place once a year and only among cows that
are half-wild. In nature, the rôle of commander is
peacefully assigned to an ancient female, who is evidently
the most expert. Her rôle as guide does not confer on her
the right to dominate the other members of the group.
Crows, elks and horned animals fight for mastery only when
the authority of the head is placed under discussion. This
does not happen every year and a male often maintains his
position unchallenged for several years, even when his
wobbly old horns could easily fall at the first blow.

Among birds there are two interesting cases of reversal of
hierarchy. With certain parrots the female dominates the
male and even those on a lower rung have a right to feed
before the males on a higher social rung. This situation lasts
right up until reproduction when all rights are overturned
and the female makes way for the males without a shadow
of a dispute. Among canaries, however, the exact opposite
occurs. The males who are normally dominant, pass to a
lower position during reproduction.

Returning to insects for an instant, we discover the
existence of hierarchies in the common field cricket. It is a
linear hierarchy which establishes itself in a bloodless way.
Two crickets cross each other's antennae and strike the
front part of the adversary's body. If neither one of them
yields, they start intoning a war chant and the strongest
bites the weakest, throwing him to one side although not

killing him. The winner then monopolises the chosen female and will not let anybody touch her, with one exception: if the loser possessed her before, he keeps his rights over her in spite of everything, and the dominant one does not come near.

A strictly matriarchal hierarchy can be seen among stags. However long and powerful his horns, a male stag will never become head of the group – a position which is always reserved for the oldest female deer. But when, however, the males head off towards the females' territory which stands apart, the first to arrive has the right to collect a harem together. When the other males arrive, there is a distribution of about ten females to every male. The strange thing is that when there is danger, the females take refuge around the head of their group, totally ignoring the males who either follow the females or flee. The male group rarely has a recognised leader and is generally divided into small groups according to age.

The concentric divisions of Macaque monkeys is very interesting. It is rigid and strictly respected. The centre is occupied by the females and the young of both sexes, sometimes with the addition of some large males. The other males and the 'puppies', i.e. those that are no longer babies but not yet adult, have to stay on the periphery of the circle with the oldest ones near the inside and the youngest in the place of least respect. The babies have all the rights and can go where they want and they profit by it. The passage between the state of childhood and sub-adult for the monkeys is a sad one because they go from a state of having all the rights to no longer having any at all. During the day, the distribution does not undergo any changes and is maintained even during mealtimes. Each one keeps to his established position in respect of the others. By night when it is time to go to sleep, the monkeys form a ceremonial procession: first the dominant males set out with their females and their young: then the males of the immediately inferior rung go to the middle of the circle and accompany the remaining females with their children. When these have departed, some males from the lowest order remain behind allowing the young ones finally to enter the circle and to go off with the females left by the others.

This procession is always carried out in the same way, and the less important apes are careful not to move off before the group of 'elders' do. During the march to find food, the concentric structure is of necessity reduced to a line: the first group is formed of medium-sized males; the dominant males follow with the females and the smallest children (those that are still in arms and those who can barely walk); then comes a third group of young apes, and finally a rearguard, formed again of medium-sized males. During the day there is a type of police force which maintains order and prevents the inferiors from penetrating the ranks of their superiors. The young ones on the periphery of the circle amuse themselves with rough games which serve to determine their social level.

These monkeys have a curious way of establishing their supremacy; the submissive male puts himself in the position of the female and the dominant monkey pretends to mate with it: it could be that, initially the act really did take place but that now it is reduced to a rapid gesture which is purely symbolic, a sort of salute which takes place nearly every morning to re-establish the order of the circle.

Baboons too have their own precise hierarchy and their processions are similar to those of the Macaque monkeys, but in a different order. First come the inferior males, with several young ones, then the females with other young ones: then the dominant males follow with the females, the babies and the adolescents. After this vanguard come the females with their newborn, forming the core of the procession and finally a rearguard marshalled exactly like the vanguard. The march is rounded off with some dominant males. The hierarchy extends into the sexual field as well: a female on heat goes to offer herself to the dominant male; if he pleases her then all is fine: if not, it is not difficult to find another husband. Battles for the possession of a female are rather rare and only happens when the hierarchy is not yet definitively established.

Those enormous and strong animals, gorillas, according to those who have seen them from close quarters, are among the most peaceful and legendary animals that exist. But do not look them in the eyes: with all apes this is a sign of scant respect and of menace. Their hierarchy is not very structured when they march. Generally, a male of about 10 years is found at the head of the group, or sometimes several followed by the females, then the young males and then the young. Inside the group, relations are very peaceful indeed. It is very rare that there is competition for females and food is always abundant, gorillas being strict vegetarians, so there can be no motives for dispute. Hierarchies confine themselves to a right of presence and a fixed place to sit. If this is contravened, they receive a small slap on the back and a brief look right in the eyes immediately restores order. For the rest, the hierarchy is defined with colours. The males with grey backs dominate all the others, the females and the males with black backs dominate the young ones and a silver-backed male is the absolute head. Whatever he does, all the others follow suit.

Among baboons, one of the signs of respect consists of stroking the fur. An adult female is permitted to stroke the fur on the head of the pack with two hands, while males even of a very exalted social position, can only use one finger. Young males can only look on.

Wolves, too, have a very rigid caste system: their every position and gesture responds to precise and strict rules. The position of the head, the ears, the fur standing on end, the wrinkling of their foreheads, the gnashing of the teeth and the way they hold their tails – all these are ritual gestures. If a wolf of lowly rung approaches the Big Chief with its tail erect, it risks being condemned to death; its tail must remain invisible from end to end and be kept under its paunch. On the other hand the wolf of the middle class can let its tail hang down, but has to be careful not to raise it.

Among cows, hierarchies are much simpler: their social position depends on their age and their weight. When a new cow joins the group, she is placed on the bottom rung of the social scale however old and heavy she may be, and even if of more elevated origins.

Among South African wild dogs, hyenas and jackals, generally detested animals, with uses and habits none the less interesting for that, there are variable hierarchies whether they are among males or females. A subordinated female can become a dominating one through childbirth: and in this case is snuggled and fondled by all. And the males and females vie with each other to bring her food, offering it in the unattractive way which is so common with many animals – they regurgitate it. This pact lasts as long as there are young ones which are treated as the children of the whole group.

When the young are sufficiently grown, the mother loses her former importance and returns to her old social condition, or even lower. Matrimony can also raise the social status and when a subordinate female mates with a dominant male, the others have to respect her.

This consists of frenetic tail-wagging and licking the muzzle and the lips, in rubbing of ears and pulling of lips which are like proper smiles. In many animals – very nearly all of them – there is some type of hierarchy even if it is only a slight one. The animals which would never accept this type of constraint are cats. They can be frightened, terrorised and shaken, but they totally ignore the possibility of obeying someone else whether they be human or feline.

Perhaps a great part of sympathy and fascination for cats lies in their total and absolute independence. People who have never had cats and want to get one must remember one thing: a cat will always do what it likes. Its enemy, the mouse, will offer its stomach as a sign of submission when fighting another mouse, if it wants to save its skin; the wolf which is much larger and fiercer than the mouse, does exactly the same except that instead of offering its belly, it offers its throat, so the other can no longer strike; a cat in one of its furious amorous struggles will return home perhaps battered, bloodied and with one eye shut but certainly not submissive.

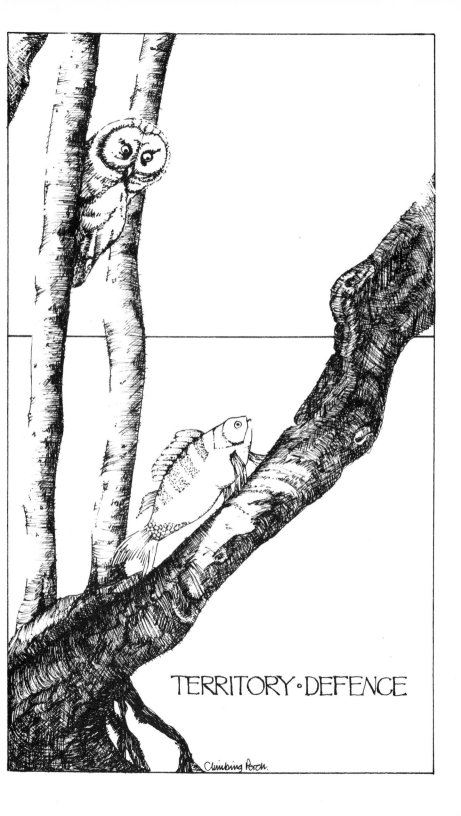

TERRITORY · DEFENCE

Climbing Perch.

CHAPTER 11

Territory and Defence

A topic that is sacred among many animals is the question of territory. Territory is the property of animals – and the small patch of earth on which they have a right to live and to die. Above all it is their hunting ground and mating place. Mammals 'scent mark' their territory with urine; others do it with glandular secretions.

The mongoose, for example sprinkles his territory with a very smelly substance and if someone deprives him of his patch, he returns immediately and does it all over again on the same spot. For some animals, territory can often be more important than love.

Some time ago an experiment regarding this was carried out on leopards. One male and one female were placed in two separate cages in a zoo. The female was on heat and the two cages were placed near each other when the amorous desires of each animal were at their climax. When the female was finally allowed to go into the male's cage, on to his territory, his sense of property was so strong that he pinned her to the floor and, with a blow of his paw, killed her.

Some insects have territories – crickets, for example. It was through defending their territory that the famous battles between crickets originated. Fish have territories too but no means of marking them and have to content themselves with appearing fierce at their boundaries. Among the fiercest defenders of fish territory are our own European stickleback and the Siamese fighting fish, which are extremely aggressive and will furiously attack anything that penetrates their boundaries.

The dimensions of a territory vary naturally according to the size and needs of its owner. A lion needs over 3,000 hectares while a group of 'shrieker' apes can make do with a hundred or so hectares. A small glow worm in the Antilles needs only 37 square metres.

Many animals are not content with marking their boundaries with urine or glandular secretions, and go to even more original lengths. The brown bear scratches all the trees on the periphery of his territory and along the ways of access, tracing out a plan, complete with road signs. This accuracy has a double edge because it is an excellent indication to hunters as to the whereabouts of the bear because they can identify him from these scratches. The European bison is even more complicated. It tears the cork and bark off trees on its boundaries with its horns and urinates the ground beneath them, then it rolls in the mud it has produced from its urine and daubs the gashes on the trees with it.

'Scent marking' the soil often serves as a sexual summons as well. In the presence of a female it wants to conquer, the male will mark a tuft of grass with urine. If the female does the same, it means she has accepted his invitation. When the owner of a territory dies, his successor generally maintains the existing marked-out limits.

The defence and marking of a territory becomes more varied and more interesting with birds. The stork prohibits other storks from entering its territory but will allow birds of other species to do so. While territories normally serve as a function of hunting and of love, they also serve as an anti-theft device among birds which live in colonies. Many birds like penguins and pelicans are incorrigible thieves, not only of food but also of stones. In such a case, the territory must have an inhibiting function to make the would-be robber aware that it would be committing not one but two infringements. Defence of territory naturally has the upper hand even over hierarchical laws, and if a dominating animal invades the territory of a dependent, it will be fiercely chased away like any other creature.

Invasion of a territory, at times, means the invasion of a wife, especially among seagulls, who are particularly quarrelsome fellows. The 'foreign' seagull sometimes even has the effrontery to try and mate with the female right under the nose of its spouse, which has to fight for its territory, and its honour at the same time. Female cormorants are faithful spouses and if they are assailed by a stranger in the absence of their mate, they employ a tactic which is usually very effective. First, they defend themselves energetically; then, if the male is too strong, they let them go ahead but acting as if they were an inanimate object, opposing his advances with passive resistance which is so irritating for the intruder that he finishes by renouncing his cockeyed project.

There is a small fish called the red swordtail which is normally kept in aquariums and is very conscious of its territory and social position. It scrupulously observes the rights of precedence and knows which fish it can dominate and which ones it is forced to submit to.

Defence and Attack

The law of survival is the first and most important lesson for any animal to learn. It is right and natural that one of the most developed instincts is that of defence. Defence can also be a form of attack and at times transforms the prey into hunter.

Among the methods of attack and defence in use in the animal world, some seem like science fiction and offer man himself a few hints on how to develop newer and more perfect weapons. Protective camouflage is certainly the most widespread form of defence but it is so varied and assumes so many different forms that it is interesting to examine some of them.

Many marine animals, especially crustaceans, are completely transparent and if they keep still, it is impossible to distinguish them from their backgrounds. Some animals have such clear designs on their bodies that they create a kind of optical illusion. It would be interesting to know whether these animals are conscious of their camouflage or whether they just keep still through fear in the presence of their enemy, ignorant that nature is working for their safety.

Many animals pretend to be dead in the presence of danger and roll over on their backs and shut their eyes. They do it so well that they often deceive their enemy. There are animals whose coat is a natural camouflage, like the leopard which inspired the American fighting uniform in the Second World War, or the giraffe which mingles easily with trees. Then there are particular animals like the sole and the chameleon which can change their colour to match their background. But in these cases there is a problem: does the animal itself decide to change colour or does its pigmentation change automatically through fear?

Disguise as inanimate objects is useful since animals have no interest in such objects. A large fish is not interested in algae or the excrement of another fish so the small fish which manages to masquerade as one of these will be safe. There is a seahorse which seems to be covered completely with excrement like algae, and which hide it totally if it keeps still. Some insects and spiders take on the exact aspect of bird excrements.

Many animals with beautiful colours alight on flowers and assume the aspect of that flower and wait there for their prey. Others are similar to twigs, leaves and petals. The most interesting example is the green or pink hemiptera which fixes itself on to the stele of plants with the pink individuals at the bottom and the green ones at the top and together they look like clusters of flowers. Many butterflies hide the gaudy colour of their wings beneath another pair which makes them pass completely unnoticed. Other butterflies absorb the repellant odour of the plants on which they alight and in this way keep their aggressors at bay.

Sometimes camouflage almost approaches masquerade. If there is one animal in the animal kingdom that deserves a prize for the best disguise it should go without a doubt to the forked-tail puss moth caterpillar. Deprived of defence like other caterpillars, it would be an easy prey for birds, if it were not for its disguise. It places itself in a position so that it looks like a small alligator: then it raises its rather large head on which false nostrils are designed and white blots looking like sharp teeth and the body appears to be covered with scales. Not only do birds not dare to attack it but they fly away terrified.

There is a locust in South America which adopts more or less the same method: on its back, as though painted, it has two enormous eyes which look like bird's eyes. As animals which chase locusts are rarely the same as those which chase birds, locusts can therefore go about their business undisturbed. Harmless snakes also have recourse to cunning since they do not possess the mortal weapons of muscle or poison that their colleagues do. The rubber boa is a completely peaceful snake and rolls up when it is in danger with its tail sticking out and its head hidden. It does this knowing that the enemy always strikes at the head and that, in its haste, it will quite probably not realise the difference. The grass snake, which is just as innocuous, swells up hoping to frighten its adversary away. If the trick does not work, it has another one up its sleeve: it rolls over exposing its belly and pretends to be dead.

The ostrich worm, like the millipede, is completely defenceless, and instead of fleeing, becomes immobile hoping to pass unnoticed. Its name derives from the fact that it draws its head into its body hiding it as ostriches are supposed to; but in the latter supposition we are dealing with a mistaken belief since a man who has bred ostriches for over 50 years, affirms that he has never seen an ostrich hide its head in the sand.

The cowfish is endowed with an incredible anti-capture device. If a fish larger than itself swallows it, it swells rapidly with water and air and its skin becomes covered with such sharp prickles that its captor is constrained to spit it out.

There are different animals who prefer to exploit the protection of others to defend themselves from danger. The Australian blackcap for example will only build its nest in the neighbourhood of a wasps' nest, thus getting the best armed protection it can have. The trumpet fish in its own way is also an exploiter whether it is hunting or defending itself. It will climb unnoticed on to the back of another harmless fish, getting transport and wait until the right moment to leap on to its prey which is unaware of the danger, while the trumpet-fish remains safe from probable aggressors. But when it is a matter of defending their nests and eggs, animals develop noteworthy cunning and sometimes, although rare, they develop a rather pathetic ingenuity. Terns, for example, surround their nests with beautiful shells not as decoration but in an attempt to camouflage their only egg, hiding it with the first things they can find even though they only vaguely resemble eggs.

The Australian woodpecker, on the other hand, has simplified things even further and makes its nest in tree trunks, dressing up the opening with vegetable fibres and pieces of bark, skilfully camouflaging it.

Wasps adapt their nest to their surroundings. If it is built on a house, then the nest will be the same colour as the walls, or the same colour as the object to which it is attached.

Among methods of defence which could be defined as science fiction, there is one used by a type of butterfly which is a favourite prey of bats. No one knows how, but it warns the bat by means of ultrasonic sound of its own disgusting odour. This type of communication which furnishes information about taste through sound, is certainly one of the most interesting mysteries in relations between animals, as we have seen already with dolphins.

Nature's resources in safeguarding its species are infinite: there are tiny fish which are protected by a layer of mucus and live among the tentacles of sea anemones which are poisonous for those who do not have the same protection as these fish. Here we can see the efficacy of natural selection: the animal that is the best defended or best camouflaged, survives and reproduces in great numbers. But how does the poor, enormous elephant manage to camouflage itself? It is clearly impossible and its only weapons are its intelligence and its strength – strength because it realises how much it has and what it is capable of, and intelligence which it uses to put as much force and strength as possible into display. Another large animal which is peaceful although rather disagreeable is the rhinoceros. Everything is stacked against it: it is ugly, clumsy, of frightening strength and totally lacking in any friends except for the tick bird or oxpecker, a small bird which settles on its back and picks out the ticks harbouring in its skin. It also serves as an alarm bell. If someone with warlike intentions approaches the sleeping rhino, the tick bird wakes the rhino and warns him with a loud squawking. But even this could present a death sentence for the rhino. The poor beast is, in fact, nearly blind and when a hunter approaches with a gun, before he has had time to fire, or to reload, the rhino has been warned by the tick bird's song and disappears in the nick of time. There is certainly little to joke about if a rhino charges, but it rarely manages to do this with any success because of its bad eyesight.

Even the rhino has its own magic – that something which endears it to those who are prepared to let themselves become endeared. The rhino is the easiest African animal to domesticate. It is perhaps because of its extreme solitude that it hardly ever meets anyone ready to take notice of it, or who does not flee at the first glimpse. But it makes friends easily and will approach to have its ears scratched or will roll over on its back so its tummy can be tickled. It is also always ready to play but in that case you will need to be careful it does not lean affectionately on you because it weighs 30 kilogrammes at birth. Apart from the white hunter, the rhino's great enemy is the native: the belief still persists in many regions that, when ground down, the rhino's horn is a powerful aphrodisiac, and the natives hunt it without mercy. It is grotesque that such an ugly animal should serve for such erotic ends, but then man's credibility can reach unimaginable limits.

The rhino has a sweet and timid voice, in huge contrast to its physical appearance. When it communicates with other rhinos it lets out a weak bleating which is imperceptible to the human ear. If it is young and in danger it howls like a slaughtered pig and you can witness a corporate feeling even among rhinos for all run to the defence of the little one which is in danger.

The cattle egret is also a friend of the rhino as is the tickbird. The rhino serves as a means of transport for it and it feeds off the insects the rhino turns up on his journeys. But it is not self-interest alone that binds it to this large animal. Some scholars have discovered that there is something there resembling affection. When the rhinoceros dies and is of no further use to the tickbird, this bird stays for a while on the rhino's body as though not wanting to abandon him, and to show that at least there is a minimum of affection and friendship which is the due of every creature capable of feeling in the universe.

Attack

Animals' hunting methods are infinite and each, in its own

way, is interesting. But the most notable are those which articulate themselves through different and consecutive actions, implying a form of reasoning or at least of association. The anaconda, from tropical America, for example, one of the largest of snakes has very astute hunting techniques. It hunts almost exclusively near rivers choosing its prey from among animals which drink there. When an animal approaches the river for a drink, the snake accosts him underwater, emerges rapidly and squeezes him in a flash. Then he dips into the water again and drowns his prey.

A kindred but much more complicated method is the one used by one of the strangest animals in existence in India and Malaysia – the anabasis or climbing perch. It is called a climbing fish because it is effectively a fish even though it is endowed with faculties fish do not normally possess. Not only can it climb out of the water, but it can also walk using the short, robust tips on its fins and it climbs trees. It is from trees that it gets most of its food. It settles down on a branch and remains completely immobile letting itself become covered with ants. Suddenly it dives into the water and captures and eats the ants at its leisure.

The paper nautilus, a marine animal resembling a plant, can easily capture the tiny animals it feeds off as they get entangled in the thick web of what they think are branches, but are its feet or tentacles instead. When wolves are on the warpath they trick their enemy with a strategic manoeuvre: they go towards the area where they intend making an attack and travel in Indian file so they leave what seems to be only one set of footprints but which is in reality the footprints of twenty wolves.

Any hunter will tell you of the tactics buffalos have developed after years of flight from man, having learned man's weak points. A buffalo which is wounded by a gun, i.e. by man, knows it must succumb and helps itself through cunning. The buffalo pretends to escape and as the hunter follows him, he executes a rapid semi-circle and attacks the hunter in the shoulders, having learned that surprise is the only way of survival.

We come now to that method of fighting which man has only discovered relatively recently but which animals have practised for ages: chemical warfare. The first animal we know about which uses chemical substances in defence and attack is the cuttle-fish. It is rather obvious since its ink is black and it is easy to then realise it can serve as a hiding place.

Then come electric rays, known since the time of Socrates and Plato, which shoot out electric discharges at their enemy, temporarily immobilising them. But there are still more dangerous and mortal weapons. The spitting cobra, instead of biting, spits its venom in the enemy's face from quite a distance away. The cobra's poison, which normally attacks the nervous system, paralysing the heart and the lungs, does not enter the bloodstream in this case but paralyses the sight, bringing on temporary blindness which is sufficient to allow the cobra to appropriate the victim who is no longer able to flee.

The hydra viridis, a freshwater octopus, sometimes called the machine-gun octopus, fires a poisoned pellet when its body is touched or bruised by a possible enemy, and fires it with such force that it penetrates the flesh of its attacker.

There is also the tropical frog which is extremely small and can squirt poisoned saliva from up to 4 metres away. Perhaps the most science fiction-like of animals is the cuttle-fish whose saliva contains sepia, a toxic substance which completely paralyses its prey. When the bomber dung-beetle is pursued by its enemy, it lets out a cloud of acid vapour or tear gas.

But the king of chemical warfare is that graceful animal, dear to the heart of all Walt Disney fans, the polecat. Its weapon is perfect and is situated in two glands placed under its tail and surrounded by strong muscles. When the polecat is attacked, its muscles contract and the two glands spray out a yellowish liquid which has an absolutely repugnant smell. This spray can reach a distance of 3 metres and can be repeated up to six times one after another, after which the glands have to refill. But it is rare that an enemy can resist six showers of this obnoxious smell.

ORIENTATION·MIGRATION

"Owl.

CHAPTER 12

Orientation and Migration

Animal orientation is something which still perplexes many scientists today, and they have made vain attempts to understand the secret. All the explanations and suppositions that have been advanced until now have been shown to be without foundation and insufficient. There is a risk that certain species of animals could become extinct without ever revealing their secret.

The carrier-pigeon, for example, is a bird which is now almost a myth. Everyone has heard about them but few have seen any. This unspeedy means of communication, which is probably more certain to arrive than today's post, is rapidly disappearing, in spite of the fight for its survival by the few who feel passionately about it. It is easy to confuse the carrier-pigeon with the common pigeon, which it closely resembles. But experts can distinguish between them instantly for although the carrier-pigeon is the same colour, it stands more erect, has a longer neck and its muscles are more developed and constitute half the weight of the entire bird. Their eyesight is also sharper and their lungs more powerful. The only thing we know about carrier-pigeons is that their instinct to return home makes them take the shortest possible time, when covering quite considerable distances. But no one has yet discovered the secret of this instinct.

The hypotheses are many and varied. There are those who say pigeons orientate by using the magnetic field of the earth; others maintain that a pigeon-loft emanates mysterious radiations on a particular wavelength which the birds can intercept up to 1,600 miles away. The only thing that has been proved with any degree of certainty is that pigeons need the sun to steer by. If they are set loose on a beautiful, clear day, pigeons immediately point themselves in precisely the right direction, but when the sky is overcast, they often fly against telephone and high tension wires and when it snows they lose their way completely.

A male pigeon which is separated from its mate will fly like a streak of lightning to return to her. There is a beautiful story which illustrates how orientation can be aided by love. Several years ago a pair of Danish pigeons took part in a contest in which they had to return home from a starting point in Sweden. The weather was cloudy and while the female managed to return, her companion got lost. Although the weather worsened, the next morning the female disappeared flying off in search of her companion. And, one still does not know how, but in the vastness of the sky between Sweden and Denmark, she managed to find him.

It must have been a proud day for man when he invented radar but nature preceded him by several thousand years. Bats have been endowed with a radar system since they first appeared on earth although, as with dolphins, it is more appropriate to call it a sonar system.

In 1794, Spallanzani had already demonstrated that bats orientated themselves by hearing, but it had not then been discovered that they reacted to frequencies man cannot even hear. The way in which bats manage to avoid small and immobile obstacles in the complete dark has something of the science fiction about it. Their method of hunting is even stranger; in complete darkness they catch on average one insect every ten seconds. One would think that with their exceptional hearing bats would be guided by the imperceptible noises made when their prey moved, but this is not so. With their ultrasonic emissions, bats have a complete panoramic sounding of all the space around them and receive echoes from the bodies present in the space they direct themselves at. They hardly ever make mistakes. If, exceptionally, a bat misses an insect the first time round, it immediately corrects its flight course and then never errs the second time. At times, it uses its wings to snatch up the insect and carry it to its mouth.

Pye, an English physiologist, has compared the bat to a self-guided missile. But no human product, even though perfected and produced after long years of research and study, could have the perfection of these living missiles which, with the maximum naturalness, hunt in circumstances which would be impossible for man. Bats hunt in rain, and, not having very good eyesight, there is a chance they could confuse a drop of water with an insect of the same size. They hunt in the most intricate forests but are not put off by the tangle of branches, leaves and flowers.

Not all bats have the same means of orientation. The two basic types which have been studied are the genus vespertilio and the genus rhinolophus. The first type have fixed ears and let out numerous short cries on a modulated frequency. If they are deprived of the use of one ear, they lose their sense of orientation altogether and act as if they were totally deaf. The rhinolophus bats, on the other hand, are even more perfect and can function with one ear only which is movable and let out cries at a constant frequency, which are longer and less numerous. They can also discover obstacles and prey at greater distances.

As so much has been said about bats we must add a few words on owls. They, too, orientate by sound but in a different way. Roger Payne, a university student, discovered this many years ago. Not being able to understand how the owl, which does not have exceptional eyesight, never missed its prey in the absolute darkness, Payne decided to experiment. He shut all the doors and openings in a long shed, so there was complete dark, scattered some dry leaves on the ground and set the owl free. When he turned on the lights after a few minutes, the owl was no longer on his roost and had a mouse in his talons. Then Payne tried to discover whether the owl was guided by smell or by invisible waves of heat as certain snakes are. When all his experiments proved negative, he tried blocking up one of the owl's ears. The owl missed a lot of prey with his ear blocked like this. The hearing of the owl depends greatly on the shape of the ear which is different from that of the bat. An owl's face is covered with discs of feathers which pick up sound waves which rebound in the ear-drum. The largest ear-drums in existence can be found in the world of birds.

If one considers that the invention of the magnet took place in the twelfth century when birds had already been flying and travelling peacefully for millions of years without any instrument other than the sun, then this is the moment in which man realises that all his science accumulated over many thousands of years, is diminished beside the simple instinct of birds.

It was not until the eighteenth century that man realised that a great number of birds flew during the night. They do not fly alone but prefer to migrate then. The interest in migration is growing and so are the examples which become more and more incredible and are accompanied by careful observations. The grey partridge, which is born at about 12° from the North Pole, leaves its nest when it is 42 days old and reaches the ice-floes of the Antarctic 17,000 kilometres away where it spends the winter. In the summer it returns to exactly the same spot solving problems of navigation which man has not been able to understand for thousands of years. The world record for returning home has to go to the stormy petrel which builds its nest on a promontory on the Welsh coast. One such bird was taken by aeroplane to Boston and set free on June 4, 1952. Twelve days later, having crossed the ocean, it reached its nest after journeying for 4,900 kilometres.

Experiments have also been done by using artificial suns and seeing whether, after it is shown to birds, they followed the light of the natural sun, or the artificial sun. It is already a step forward, although still a mystery, how birds can use the position of the sun even by night. It is difficult enough to navigate by the sun during the day, since the sun is continually changing its position. In fact, the bird which gets its bearings from the sun undertakes a whole series of calculations which only an electronic calculator would be able to do for man. The biologist, Matthews, from Cambridge University, has given us a plausible explanation for flying at night. He says orientation of flight by night is deduced from the sun during the day and maintained as far as possible during darkness by referring to the moon and the stars.

A contrary hypothesis was made by a German ornithologist. His experiments using the warbler songbird, which travels huge distances especially by night, showed that it took its bearings from the stars as much as from the sun and that if they saw a planet instead, they turned immediately in the direction which, on the planet, would correspond to their winter quarters.

Fish migrations pose an even more arduous problem than those of birds; because of their limited vision of the landscape fish do not have the sun or the stars to steer by. The most interesting case is that of salmon which are capable of finding their own river after a sojourn of several years in the high seas. The only way to undertake such an observation is to mark the largest number of young fish possible. They return 'home' at the time of reproduction because salmon, like several other animals, prefer to reproduce in their birthplace. Naturally, many explanations have been given to this phenomenon, as to that of birds: but the mystery still remains, even here.

Some people maintain that salmon have extremely acute olfactory equipment, and trust in their own sense of smell to find their own river from a great distance away. Others say that the physical or chemical peculiarities of the water play a determining part in this recognition and that salmon are therefore able to recognise the oxygen or carbon dioxide content or the salt concentration of the water.

Experiments have effectively shown that it is possible to condition very young salmon by pouring a small quantity of a chemical substance into the river and the salmon will always search for the places where this substance can be found. Another experiment was made by taking a group of salmon and dividing them into two. One of the groups had their nasal apertures stopped up with cotton, and then the two groups were marked with different signs and set free. The normal salmon found their original rivers without any difficulty while the others did not.

Even if this experiment seems to support the hypothesis of those who base orientation on the sense of smell, we must not forget that the total loss of a sense in an animal, will upset the whole living structure and proof therefore cannot be definitive. On the other hand, other experiments have shown that if it is not swimming at a great depth the salmon can see the position of the sun and knows all the cardinal points.

Eels, too, are exceptional migrators. Their eggs hatch in the Sargasso Sea where European eggs mix with American eel eggs. The spawn live together for several weeks then the two species divide and each leave for their own destination.

An American eel has never been spotted in Europe or vice versa. American eels are carried by the Gulf currents and complete their journeys as far up as the river estuaries of North America within a year. European eels however, have longer journeys to undertake and which take two years. From the moment they become adults they live in freshwater until the moment when they reproduce. Then they begin the same journey in reverse and return to the Sargasso Sea.

Another interesting theory sees eel migration as being strictly linked with the theory of continental drift as stated by the German scientist, Lothar Wegener. In brief it says this: the earth's crust is composed of two layers. The outer layer is lighter and not as deep as the sea. Wegener's hypothesis is that the earth originally had a complete covering of this outer layer, but half of it was projected into space. The rest broke up into the large chunks we know as continents, which began to drift to rebalance the earth which had gone off course.

If one admits that eels originated from this breaking-up of the old world and the new, when continents were still very close together, and one concedes that the time between reproduction in the bogs and rivers and other nearby continents meant that eels had to undertake even longer journeys as the continents drifted further and further apart, then the necessity arose of having to spend a longer period in the fresh water to prepare for the long journey. This is still the situation today. Whatever instinct pushes them to the birth places of their progenitors, still after millions of years, belongs to those questions we will probably never get answers to.

Lobsters in the Gulf of Mexico undertake a slow, mini migration which one could almost call a holiday. When they are about 15 days old, the small lobsters assemble, cross the Gulf with great difficulty and reach the marshy land where they pass a period of 6–9 months. Then one night they all return together to their birthplace.

The strangest example of migration is that of the Danaide butterfly of North America. Each year, it leaves the North to go and lay its eggs in the South. After laying its eggs, the butterfly dies and the successive generation hatches and sets out towards their parents' home – a migration which stretches beyond death. But the strangest thing is that the butterflies always fly to the same trees which have no manifest physical or chemical differences from the nearby trees.

Apart from these well known animals, there are others which use differing means of orientation which are just as interesting. There are certain electric rays which are provided with an astoundingly individual system. Their organs produce currents and their receivers are able to discover variations of gradient produced by obstacles which deform the field around the animal. In this way, torpedo fish can also discover the electricity field of another fish.

Still in the water, there are those aquatic bugs, water boatmen, which can distinguish the sources of vibrations very precisely from the rows of fine hairs on their third pair of legs.

The strangest animal for its individual process is the rhyssa, a large insect from the ichneumon group of flies. The rhyssa lays its eggs in the larva of the great woodwasp, but how it finds the larva remains a great mystery to this day. Generally, the larva are found inside wood at a depth of several centimetres and it is thus impossible for them to put out any kind of signal. The rhyssa cannot pick up either visual, audio or sensual stimuli because it is impossible for the almost amorphous larva to emanate any kind of smell from a depth of several centimetres of wood. But the rhyssa which has been observed at work, searching for larva, flies here and there around the pine forest, then settles decisively on a log where it sinks its ovipositor into the wood. If one tries to check its movement after it has left, one will unfailingly find the larva with the developing rhyssa embedded in them.

Radar and sonar, electric machines and all such mechanisms although perfect and ultra sensitive, are based on a rational principle and can be understood even though they are still in a relatively unrefined state, but not that of the rhyssa. If all the animals which were endowed with these sonar devices were able to tell us of their incredible possibilities and we were able to apply them, scientists would be almost omnipotent. The incredible perception and unknown sense of direction which enables cats and dogs to undertake prodigious returns home, often appears in newspapers. There is one story I would like to tell which recounts the tale of Hector, the stowaway dog.

On April 20, 1922, in the port of Vancouver, Harold Kildall the second officer on the merchant ship *Hanley* took part in a strange event. A large black and white terrier jumped on board his ship and looked anxiously around sniffing in a frantic manner. Then he jumped off again. He repeated the same performance with all the ships in the port, evidently dissatisfied with his search because a day later, when the *Hanley* had already set sail for Japan, the dog was found in front of the commanding officer's cabin. He had obviously managed to embark unnoticed with very precise intentions. The dog was adopted by the crew but did not make friends with anyone. He accepted food and caresses but was never affectionate and seemed to be constantly preoccupied, always following Kildall but never showing him any affection. It was quite clear the dog was accustomed to sea voyages and he went around as if he were quite at home and in some way knew the ship's structure. At mealtimes, he would descend below deck to get something to eat and would then reappear looking for Kildall to follow his movements as closely as possible.

When the Japanese coastline began to appear, the dog put himself at an observation post and began sniffing attentively at the wind that was coming from the land. In the port of Yokohama, the *Hanley* tied up next to a Dutch ship called the *Simaloer* which was also carrying girders. The dog's attention became more and more acute and his eyes were fixed on the Dutch steamer. At a certain point a Japanese boat came close to the *Simaloer* and two men got off and walked towards the customs, passing right below the *Hanley*'s deck. Still watchful, the dog began to howl and then to bark even louder until finally he attracted the attention of the two men who were standing on the boat. Suddenly one of the men leapt to his feet and he, in his turn, began shouting and gesticulating to his companion. Finally, the dog could bear it no longer and jumped into the water where he was immediately pulled out and kissed by his happy master, who then told the whole story to the two stupefied crews.

W. M. Mante was the second officer on the *Simaloer* as was Kildall on the *Hanley* with the same duties and the same turns of watch. At Vancouver, before the *Simaloer* left, it had changed its moorings while the dog, Hector, was having a last-minute walk ashore. But the boat left before the dog could find it again and get on board. Losing all hope of finding his ship, Hector had searched for a ship which was carrying a similar cargo and which would be the only ship likely to carry him and perhaps reunite him with his master across the seas. So he attached himself to the officer whose turns of watch were the same as Mante's, clearly thinking he would have a greater chance of meeting him in port which is, in fact, what happened. This story is true and the sailors of both ships who are still alive, remember the episode.

Ants give us a general example of what our society would be like in the future – perfectly conditioned, ordered and thought-out – a Brave New World, in fact. Ants enter this discussion on orientation in every way because, being such perfect animals, they can naturally get their bearings very easily. Their means of orientation are firstly, the sun, and secondly, smell. They are so perfectly structured and their minuscule bodies so devised that they leave different traces when they go in search of food from when they return home, so their companions will always know which way they have gone by the smell.

The possibility of a chemical origin for orientation has been much talked of, but if this is to be plausible in regard to smaller animals and lesser distances, it is as shaky a theory as if it were on a larger scale. For example, if one understands that the larva of a fly needs water to survive, the larva will sense this necessity so strongly that it will reach a damp spot and it is difficult to imagine the blind and brainless salmon or eels in the same situation when covering thousands of miles.

Many naturalists are now convinced that there is an undiscovered force at work guiding living beings by influence from a sensory sphere and mechanical phenomena.

Extra sensory perception which is talked about so much today in relation to so-called 'witches' or 'seers' or persons gifted with particular faculties, is also attributed to animals, in a much larger measure than to man. However, one perceives things, it must be admitted that if we are talking about visual, audio or olfactory orientation, animals have always possessed potential that man will perhaps never have or will only achieve after thousands of years of study and research.

METEOROLOGY

Curley sheep.

CHAPTER 13

Meteorology, Foresight, Telepathy

Meteorology is a field in which man is enormously behind animals and one in which he would do better to trust in their foresight. Animals have an enormous sensitivity to atmospheric changes which is much more acute than human sensitivity and there are numerous examples to prove it.

Let us take ants as an example as they really force themselves into this discussion. It is useless to go on ignoring them and continuing to be astonished at what they know and do. I think I will raise a group of ants and try to tame them to see whether or not they are complete automatons or not. In any event, to return to meteorology, you can rely absolutely on ants to anticipate rain. If you see a group of ants moving on to higher ground from where they are nesting, you can be sure that it is about to rain. Ants which know this can forsee the intensity and duration of showers, and fear floods in their areas.

Sheep, too, are strange announcers of rain but in this case there is no mysterious instinct at hand; it is simply a question that their wool which is curly when the weather is beautiful, becomes straighter when it is wet, like many people's hair.

Where animals show their major usefulness in this field (and they can really save lives if you trust them) is in foreseeing large disturbances such as hurricanes, earthquakes and avalanches which they perceive with a sixth sense. Some years ago in Gascony, several hours before a tremendous hurricane hit the Gulf all the domesticated animals were showing signs of agitation and probably saved the lives of many fishermen, who noticed and, as a result, did not put out to sea.

The sensitivity of animals regarding earthquakes has been measured by a German zoologist, Ernst Killian. He found that 5 seconds before an earth tremor, horses began to neigh and tremble. The pheasant, however, begins agitating 10 seconds before while dogs can perceive light tremors several minutes before man does. Dogs, as usual, are the most sensitive and intelligent of all animals and can evaluate the danger and run for shelter.

One of the most astounding rescues was undertaken by an avalanche dog in the terrible January of 1951 in the valley of Binn about 50 kilometres from Cervino in Italy. Several men had been swept away by an avalanche and the rescue team was out. All the victims had been pulled out, so nobody knew why the dog belonging to one of the rescuers was running backwards and forwards, whining and pulling at his master's trouser leg. Fortunately the man knew his dog well and trusted him. Immediately he ordered everyone to abandon the area as the dog required. Hardly had they left and gone away than another avalanche poured down into the place where they had been standing, covering it completely. The dog had saved twenty-two men.

On April 18, 1906, before the tremendous San Francisco earthquake many animals belonging to farmers, began running around in confusion and frantically sniffing the air; while their owners were still searching for an explanation, the earthquake occurred.

In Thessaly in 1954 an earth tremor caused several deaths, but there would have been more if the people who had been brought up in the classical tradition and knew all about prophetic animals, had not placed their faith in the fact that all the storks had flown away after behaving in a very anxious manner. This happened half an hour before the earthquake and many inhabitants understood it in time to abandon their houses.

One morning in 1939 the dogs belonging to the convent of Saint Bernard refused to follow the monks on their usual walk. An hour later, an avalanche fell down on the road where they would have passed.

And finally the cat. The warnings of cats assume major importance because they are infrequent and, because of the animals aloofness they have less possibility of communicating. One particular cat made it quite clear to his owner that not only should he leave the house immediately but he should also get as far away as possible from the district. A few seconds later, large crevices appeared in the ground and swallowed up a great number of houses.

But if it is possible to explain the forecasting of natural phenomena as a greater sensitivity or the awareness of 'waves' unknown to us, there are events that cannot be classified as natural like car crashes and aeroplane accidents.

The most famous episode is the plane accident in which the British Aviation Minister, Lord Thompson lost his life. He had a small terrier which followed him everywhere, even on planes. One day, before a trip the dog began showing terrible nervous signs and refused his food, barking and wailing desperately for no apparent reason. Just as they were about to leave the dog refused to get on the plane and hid. No prayers or entreaties could entice him out, so Lord Thompson left without him on what was to be his last trip. If he had had faith in his dog, he would not have gone or he would have suspended the flight and saved not only his own life but that of all the other people on the plane as well.

This is a hard blow for the sceptics because here we have reached the boundaries of the supernatural and are in a taboo sphere.

If an animal is in a position to warn of an accident which

is to happen in the future, and which is not to happen through natural causes, it must first mean that the writing is already on the wall and secondly that when it is written there is somebody there to read it, even if it is a dog. If a dog can do this why cannot a man or several other animals do it? If we think of the immeasurable consequences of this fact, could we avoid accidents that are already 'written' or not? What would have happened had Lord Thompson not taken the flight? These are all questions of vital importance but most people continue to ignore them either through lack of information or because they wish to ignore them. Very few people are kindly disposed to find out when they are going to die, especially whether that moment is near at hand.

Remorse and regret would well up and all the things not done and not said, and that terrible sense of it being too late already. All the Cassandras of the world would certainly become silent.

Some animals however have an exact premonition of their own death, like horses who refuse to eat the day before they are taken to the slaughterhouse; or the humble mouse which leaves the ship several hours before it sinks.

When one speaks of a 'sixth sense' one enters a minefield of paranormal phenomena. I say 'minefield' because even when it is not a matter of foresight of a near disaster being unrecognised by official science, it is also subject to indifference and scepticism and the most relentless boycotting. Sceptics usually limit themselves to saying "What I cannot see I do not believe" and then when they do see it, they decide they do not believe it all the same, because they think there must be some trick.

These are substantially harmless people. It is only fairly recently that the news was published that a lawyer who was anti-sorcery, opened an office having decided to unmask and possibly send to prison all the various wizards, prophets, healers and so on. He was perfectly right. Too many people nowadays abuse those who reach out to the occult as a last resort. But what happens if he really imprisons those who cannot be unmasked? Those who really do 'see' and really can 'heal'? Will we see the return of witchcraft trials? And will all cats, dogs and horses that foresee earthquakes be incriminated as well? When people say 'it must be a trick' most of the time, there is a trick. But need there always be? Why should we deny animals and men the possession of certain faculties which no one can ignore even though there is no explanation for them at the moment?

Gustavo Rol, the famous Turin antiquarian painter, was gifted with what everyone called 'powers' or 'faculties' and which he alone defined as 'possibilities'. This man was unique in the world and could keep perfectly still while his brush painted by itself. He affirmed that everyone has these 'possibilities' in their power but that he had simply developed and exercised them more.

Telepathy is decidedly more widespread among animals than among men. Many clever circus animals do not really know how to read or write but choose the right figures and letters through thought transference from their teacher. Here is an example of domestic telepathy. My kitten, Penny, knows quite well, when she hears me go into the kitchen whether I am going in to make coffee (which means cream for her) or to eat a grapefruit which she does not like. If that is not telepathy I do not know what is, seeing that whether it was cream or grapefruit, they are both in the 'fridge.

Telepathy between animals is even more widespread. It is also a necessary adjunct since animals are much less well provided with speech than ourselves. Sometimes it is enough for the head of a group to 'think' an order for it to be immediately understood and put into effect by the others. But for us telepathy between man and animals is certainly far more interesting since it involves us directly and since it enters paranormal spheres. We have seen that this is nearly normal between animals.

One of the most intriguing incidents, perhaps through the interest it aroused at the time is what happened to the writer, Rider Haggard in 1904. It was reported in the Journal of the Society for Psychical Research and is so significant it can be considered emblematic of the whole problem.

On the night of July 20 Rider Haggard went to bed about one o'clock. After an hour, his wife, who was sleeping in the same room woke up suddenly, hearing her husband moan in a strange way rather like a wounded animal. She woke him up to free him from what was evidently a nightmare and he told her what he had dreamed. He had seen his daughter's old black retriever, Bob, struggling as though rebelling against a violent death. He said he saw Bob stretched out on his side among the canes in a swamp. It seemed as if he himself had killed the dog in some mysterious way from the manner in which the dog's head was raised strangely towards his face. Bob tried to talk to him but not succeeding in making himself understood, transmitted to Rider Haggard, in a way he could not define the notion that he was dying. Then Haggard went back to sleep and slept tranquilly without any further nightmares. The next day he told his daughter about his dream but she was not worried because she had seen her dog in excellent shape the evening before. But Bob did not appear at breakfast or ever again. They began to search for him in vain and then, four days later, the poor dog was found floating in a swamp where he had gone to die with his legs shattered and his skull split open after a train had hit him. His bloodied collar was found by a workman on a railway bridge and so they were able to reconstruct the episode. The only explanation was that of thought transmission and identification between man and dog, excluding any telepathic transmission on the part of those present at the accident since none of them had been aware of the fact. One can also exclude the possibility of distant perception because in this case the spectator assisted passively at the event. We have seen that Rider Haggard was so identified with the dog in his dream that it seemed to him that his 'id' was mysteriously coming out of the dog's body.

Naturally one takes into account the particular sensitivity of the writer, which made him particularly receptive, but no one doubts that this treats of a case of telepathy. There are also several episodes in which it is the animal (nearly always a dog) which receives the transmission from man. But even these, unfortunately, are always tragic. Men and animals are evidently much more sensitive to sorrow than to joy although a sad reason for this but one that is near the truth, could be that sadness is much more intense and more frequent than joy.

The following episode happened when people were a little less hectic than they are now and had more time to occupy themselves with these things and to tell them. This event happened in 1905 and was told by Baron Joseph de Kronhelm, a psychology student. His friend went to fight in Manchuria and left his dog with another officer. Three months later the dog suddenly began to howl in a terrible way, one day, for no apparent reason and without anyone being able to calm him down by stroking him or giving him food which he refused for several days. A short time after, the officer received the news that his friend had died in an exchange with the Japanese on the very morning, in fact, that the dog had begun to howl.

These strange and apparently incredible episodes are much more numerous than one thinks.

I do not want to tell tales of apparitions of dead dogs or in other words, dog ghosts. To believe in the ghosts of dogs, you must first of all believe in ghosts; and since ghosts generally appear at night, it is not difficult, even with the greatest will in the world, to confuse them with dreams. But leaving this argument aside, there are stories which happened in the full light of the day and with several witnesses, which merit being told.

One is that which happened on June 17, 1951, at Spinadesco near Cremona, at the funeral of old Achille Alquanti. The old man was very religious but his sons were athiests and wanted a civilian funeral. The horses pulling the funeral cart were just passing the church when they knelt down and refused to get up and continue for some time. Evidently the dead man had transmitted to the animals his extreme desire for a religious burial which was being denied him.

We can see from this that dogs and horses have a very clear idea about the meaning of death and also of burial. And this is even more notable because if they do bury their dead as happens with certain species, it is not done with our rituals. On the other hand if one imagines that dogs, cats and horses have learned about funerals, by seeing them, the explanation becomes more difficult when one talks of wild animals in this context.

In a seaside town in England, an episode happened when the funeral of a pigeon keeper took place. He had done much to help preserve pigeons from becoming extinct and was passionately interested in them. When the service began a pigeon flew down and sat on his coffin, remaining there until the service was over.

Another time on January 4, 1952, at Murau in Styria, a young deer suddenly jumped out of the forest and joined the funeral procession of the head gamekeeper of the area. It remained there until the coffin was lowered into the ground and then disappeared among the trees. Several months previously the young orphaned deer had been found by that very same gamekeeper who had fed him and looked after him until he was able to fend for himself. Then he had set it free. The small animal could possibly have experienced death in witnessing his parents die, but there was certainly no way he could ever have been to a funeral before. Some mysterious instinct must have told him that his benefactor was shut in that box and that he had to go and salute him there for the last time as he used to do every morning, stopping for a moment in front of his house.

Reincarnation is an old argument which has always inspired students since Pythagoras and naturally has its supporters and its denigrators, and can perhaps be explained rationally as being based on the survival of nuclear acids in the body which, when it dies, transfers to another living body carrying some of the characteristics of the old body with it. But here a too complex and scientific explanation is involved; suffice it to say, therefore, that perhaps there is such a possibility for non-believers.

It is on this subject that there is a need to record the case of Peg, the puppy, who became famous in 1957 and appeared many times on Italian television demonstrating her reading skills. Of all the things Peg said and asserted, I only want to recall one. She said she was the reincarnation of a German woman, stating very clearly that in another terrible life she had been Paola. Peg remembered several German words and when taken to a house with a piano she had never seen before, was asked whether she knew what the instrument was. She replied that it was a 'clafichord' using the 'f' instead of the 'v' as Germans do.

An inexplicable mystery? Perhaps not. We are half way to explaining it, without ever needing to refer to the existence of the soul, with convincing demonstrations which could persuade even the most relentless positivists.

CHAPTER 14

Physical Characteristics, Hibernation, Medicine

Although not insensitive to pain, many animals are in a much better position to withstand it than human beings. It is not a matter of courage but of physical properties which depend on diverse factors. It seems almost certain that dinosaurs owed their extreme stupidity to their insensitivity: their enormous mass and their tiny brains reacted together in such a way that if they were attacked from behind, they did not feel any pain for several minutes because after the long journey to the small brain, the painful stimulus was almost exhaused.

The toad is totally insensitive to variations in temperature which are not rapid. If a toad is brought gradually to the boil or slowly frozen it scarcely reacts at all. It is clear this property can be very useful but also dangerous. If it can bear any temperature it could also find itself boiled or frozen without doing anything to stop it.

The giraffe, too, has some surprising qualities. It is perhaps the animal which suffers least from thirst. If there is a shortage of water, the giraffe can go for months without drinking by feeding off acacia leaves which are rich in water, without noticing their long, spiny prickles.

Amphibians are the most resistant to deprivation. In 1897 at Eastland in Texas, when a courthouse was built, a frog was imprisoned in a corner stone. Thirty years later when the cavity was reopened the frog was still there, alive and flourishing. Although it died a year later.

Tortoises have a good resistance. They suffer from the cold but in recompense can bear heat, hunger, drought and various amputations. The most ascetic animal we know of lived for 6 years without eating. It was a giant turtle from the Galapagos Islands which generally feeds off grass, but sometimes chews some cactus leaves as an apéritif, because the spines stimulate its gastric juices. Another animal which eats strange things is the octopus: it often eats its own arms which grow again.

The Australian cockroach is like a fakir and can walk calmly over burning branches without noticing it. On the other hand, the salamander is decidedly removed from the picture superstition paints. It is untrue that it can walk through flames quite easily because of its damp skin. It can resist them for a short while but even the salamander burns.

The physical peculiarities of animals never cease to amaze and the most gifted are those endowed with strange faculties, and the ones that are nearly always furthest away from man. For example, there are poisonous snakes which not only never die from other poisonous snake bites but are also insensitive to the bite itself.

The humming bird is normally hot-blooded but if the temperature drops too much, instead of migrating, it takes up its old reptilian nature and becomes cold-blooded again. Regeneration is another of the most important and interesting of animals faculties. Everybody knows that a glow worm in flight prefers to leave its tail behind, knowing perhaps that it will grow again. But this phenomenon is common with more animals than one thinks. It was first studied by Trembley in 1740 in now classic experiments in which he set out to discover whether the hydra was a vegetable or an animal. Trembley cut the hydra into pieces and showed that from every three to four pieces another three new hydra would grow.

Nature seems to follow a law of compensation because regeneration is so frequent even in the simplest of organisms. But it is rarer in the more complex organism and practically non-existent in birds, mammals and man. In protozoa, each part of the body is made up of cytoplasm and nuclear materials and is capable of regenerating. In the simple metazoa regeneration has already become less simple. Two materials must be present: ectoderm and endoplast which constitute the wall of the animal's body. In other invertebrates, it is always necessary to have a great number of tissues since only the tail and the hind legs can be re-created. This process happens far more easily with fish than with reptiles, which can regenerate their tail and hind limbs but not the front ones.

One particularly interesting process where regeneration is limited to reproduction alone is found in certain types of sponges which, when filtered through a fine gauze, separate themselves completely to pass through and then reunite into a complete individual again the other side. In jellyfish each piece that is cut produces a smaller jellyfish. An animal closer to humans is the starfish which has a high capacity for regrowth; when its central disc is deprived of arms, it grows them all again. This is the reason why starfish are always complete when found, and break when they have been dried and dessicated.

Amphibians can regenerate the crystalline in their eyes and trytons can reproduce their eyeballs. Glow worms regenerate their tails but a different one from the tail before. Are these animals science fiction? It may seem that way, but they are alive and real, although many of them are so far from our concept of animals that we could confuse them with plants, if we had not studied them at school. I still remember my astonishment when I was told that corals and sponges which I was used to seeing motionless on the sand were animals like cats and dogs but differently structured.

Asexual reproduction is even more interesting than regeneration. If you see a protozoa reproducing itself by fission, dividing itself into two, each one of which divides itself into two again, in which there is always a tiny fragment of the original, one cannot help but reflect that these simple organisms are superior to man and hold the key to the secret of immortality.

As we are on a theme with affinities to reproduction, here would be the place to pause and return to the question of the animal peculiarity of sex change. Besides mutations, which happen in hermaphrodite animals where, in the same individual, the characteristics of one sex mature first and then those of the other, there are real sex reversals in some animals. Some occur through genetic causes, some through physiological causes and some through pathological causes.

Genetic reversal has been studied principally in the gypsy moth butterfly and results show it to be a regular and constant phenomenon. The individual butterfly begins life developing the characteristics of one sex, then at a certain point, a reversal occurs and it continues developing with the other sexual characteristics. At the start, it can be either masculine or feminine then gradually the organs of the opposite sex develop and the ones they already possess are transformed.

A similar phenomenon happens with certain types of frogs which begin to develop as females and then during their first or second year of life, about half of them change sex so that when reproduction occurs, there are the right number of both sexes. Sometimes inversion happens too late and is not completed so hermaphrodite individuals are born. But even this is not a proper anomaly since hermaphroditism is common in all amphibia. Toads have decidedly female organs and can develop eggs in their testicles.

Several insects, crustaceans and fish are the same, but it is more common for females to turn into males.

Reversal through physiological causes is generally due to the presence of parasites and has been imprecisely labelled 'parasitic castration'. It is widespread among males while females undergo almost no change. Males become totally female because this parasite completely destroys the testicles. If the animal recovers from this infection, the testicles can grow again, but they will no longer be adapted to reproduction, and will, in fact, produce eggs instead of spermatazoa.

But why do parasites cause this sex reversal? The most obvious explanation is that they modify the male metabolism causing it to produce a greater quantity of fat, which occurs in females when they have to protect their eggs. This fat production brings about the loss of secondary sexual characteristics and the male becomes more and more feminine. But the phenomenon of testicles transforming into ovaries is much more difficult to explain. One would imagine the male's sexual constitution to be much less stable than the female's, and that female characteristics, always latent, would be ready to go into action when the occasion demanded it.

The strange case of the bonellia worm is too interesting to neglect. The female is several centimetres long while the male is a different shape and measures only a few millimetres. An indistinguishable larva is born from the eggs which can develop as either female or male. If the larva settles on the proboscis of an adult female within three days of its birth, it develops into a male; if however, it stays free and hides in the sand, it grows into a female. It seems that the substance sucked from the female has the property of masculinising it. Sex change can also happen in adult animals through physiological or pathological causes, although sex changes in doves are even rarer and generally due to serious pathological causes, such as tumours or tuberculosis.

As cave men used to exist and perhaps still do in some remote parts of the world, so cave animals still exist and constitute a particularly interesting phenomenon. Among these 'cave dwellers' are protozoa, which being made up of simple organisms are found practically everywhere, but are less interesting for use because it is difficult to see them and we naturally do not consider them as animals. But they are not the only ones to live in caves. There are also several species of crustaceans, scorpions, spiders, several molluscs, fish, bats and mice. But the interest aroused by these animals is not so much their presence in caves as their immediate adaptation to their surroundings. One of the most common characteristics is the regression of the whole visual organ which is present in different states and depends on the length of time the species stays in the dark.

This regression ranges from the disappearance of eye pigmentation to the complete lack of sight and can account for huge claws or antennae and very acute hearing.

Another peculiarity these animals possess is depigmentation. The animals are all whitish except for the transparent ones which assume a pink colour because you see the blood through their skin. These animals generally need constant temperatures, feed off fungus and mould and flee from the light.

Animals know what is going on around them by means of light, sounds, heat, chemical substances and electrical fields. These are the principle vehicles of information. Insects, for example, perceive the smell of food by means of hairs on their legs. Feeling is often the least developed sense.

The scorpion, however, uses its feeling to sample the consistency of the sand in which it will lay its eggs and is equipped for this with suitable 'tactile combs'. Also those splendid but dangerous animals, sea anemones, use their sense of touch in a rather strange way. All is lost for the prey which touches their tentacles. It is immediately captured and left without any possibility of escape, is paralysed and devoured. There are a few animals which use paralysing substances either for defence or for attack. These substances have not yet been properly examined and their use enters in the science fiction techniques we defined earlier as chemical warfare. There are some snakes which can strike their prey in the dark, by relying entirely on their own sensitivity to heat variations. Among these are rattlesnakes and boa constrictors. Think, then, of the enormous dangers they represent by day and by night. To this end they are endowed with small cells found on the nose, in a dimple on their side in rattlesnakes and in different spots on the boa. The emerald green boa can observe objects with a temperature of 0.2° above the atmosphere they are in. Among animals gifted with some of the most acute senses are catfish, those freshwater scavengers, which are covered with very long, poisonous hairs. The senses of the catfish are more developed than those of humans. It has exceptional eyesight which enables it to see perfectly what is happening above it; it can hear the noise of small crabs in their mother's womb, and furthermore knows exactly what depth it is swimming at, and using some unknown sixth sense, can hear fish moving far away. Then there is its sense of taste: it has sensory appendices like barbels or cats whiskers, with which it continually savours the mud, and everything around it, whether vegetable, animal or artificial. But it is not only whiskers this petty monarch of the palate uses to savour things, but all the skin on its body, with or without scales, which it can taste with and the tongue-shaped tail, too, is used in the same way.

Jean George, who studied this strange fish, quotes the comment of one fisherman: "The catfish can savour the crayfish with its mind, the mussels with its side, while the tail slavers over a mouthful of turtle. There is no part of the catfish which is not capable of tasting something."

Even the sense of smell is very developed in this exceptional animal. At first sight it would appear impossible to smell underwater but a fish's olfactory equipment is different to ours and allows water to go in and out of its nose until they detect a smell. This curious glutton is naturally one of the easiest prey for fishermen because it approaches to taste everything. However, it's one excellent weapon of defence is its tremendous spines which can inflict painful wounds. The catfish's more enviable feature is its lateral line, a type of tube which runs the length of its body. Most fish have them and you can recognise them from their design or different colours. But in no fish is it as perfect as in the catfish.

Nerves and pores are attached to this tube which carries vibrations to the fish of distant objects. The catfish is informed of everything that happens in the water and on the ground. It can even hear the footsteps of the fisherman along the river bank, or the beetle nibbling water lilies, the chaffinch warbling, the slow worm rustling in the grass and the patter of frogs' tiny feet.

But one secret man will probably never know is how the lateral line can communicate what is happening far away through tactile perception. It can feel by touch everything that happens far away as if it were actually touching the objects in question themselves. Another important function of the lateral line is that of a thermostat. It tells fish exactly when spring arrives, what the temperature is and how long the fish should stay in the same place and get used to the change in temperature. If modern ships had a lateral line at their disposal, all their radar and sonar systems would be unnecessary.

The catfish is also gifted with incredible resistance. While it can eat anything and is a species of aquatic ostrich, it can also put up with conditions which would be fatal for anything else. It survives drought by remaining buried in mud for several months. We know that some have been buried in ditches for up to six months and have still been alive afterwards. Although the catfish is considered one of the ugliest animals alive it certainly does not lack in the fascination every science fiction creature holds. Man cannot help but admire it with astonishment and without any of its secrets being revealed.

Hibernation

Hibernation is one of the strangest and most mysterious faculties of animals. Let us look at some signs of how this type of sleep which is similar to death, comes about. I first knew about hibernation when I was a child. I adored animals and the only one I was allowed to have was a tortoise. It was not exactly the soft, warm affectionate bundle I had dreamed of but I loved it all the same. Neither was it very communicative and would only push out its head to eat and withdrew it again to sleep. When it went into hibernation in winter, it was a magical rite for me and was bewitching and naturally inexplicable. All I knew was that during hibernation it did not eat and I was told not to wake it for any reason. When it died, nobody realised for some time because it was so like its state of hibernation. It is also extremely difficult to hear a tortoise's heartbeat.

Even though it is not particularly agreeable, hibernation is one of nature's magical spells which is indispensable if certain animals are to survive. Perhaps we will soon learn how useful hibernation could be to human medicine. A scientific definition says hibernation is a 'form of latent life in hot- and cold-blooded vertebrates which is determined by extrinsic and intrinsic influences'.

There are several types of hibernations: segregations from external surroundings by drying up, changing the skin or shell; apparent death or temporary immobility under unusual or hostile stimuli; or physiological conditions of immobility and the lack of sensations which is determined by hereditary nervous action relating to the life of those hibernating.

Hibernation in certain animals corresponds to migrations in others. It is a way of escaping from dangerous climatic variations without having to remove themselves. When the water becomes too hot or too cold, certain crustaceans retire into sand holes or rock crevices for an entire season. A type of hibernation occurs in fish in that those living in freshwater lakes are not subject to migration. Many amphibia fall into a summer sleep while snails hibernate in winter to avoid the cold and in spring and summer to avoid the lack of rain. In fact, they often only wake up in the autumn.

The laziest mammal is the dormouse. To wake one from its hibernation can take more than half an hour, even using the most drastic methods. Hibernation is entirely unconnected with sleep and is completely independent of it. All animals which hibernate are fat, because they accumulate reserves which have to last them all the time they are not eating. During hibernation all the body's functions are slowed down enormously or reduced by one-third or a half. The body temperature is lowered from 30–38°C to 13–15°C. Cardiac pulsations and breathing are reduced and as all the bodily functions reduce so do the actions of poisons or harmful agents on the body. A hibernating animal can endure painful or hot physical and chemical stimuli without being aware of them – it is a perfect type of self anaesthesia. If stimuli are particularly strong an animal experiences spinal reactions which do not reach the brain and therefore do not transmit any pain. Animals can wake up with very strong stimuli. During hibernation all bodily functions continue but in a diminished way. The metabolic exchange is reduced and faecal production occurs only slightly.

The phenomenon of hibernation creates strange and often dangerous situations. For example, before it hibernates in autumn, a bear may suddenly realise it is too thin and will become dangerous when it has not accumulated enough fat to survive the winter and must look for more food as quickly as possible.

If you manage to hear an animal's heart beating during hibernation, it is so slight you might easily think it was dead and in certain situations it is as if it were.

Hibernation gives the most unexpected faculties to animals which would be of superb use if applied to man. Some experiments bear witness to these mysterious facts. A hibernating marmot was once immersed for over four consecutive hours in carbon anhydride without feeling a thing. A hibernating bat was immersed in a bucket of water for over an hour and when he was taken out, he was still asleep and his condition unchanged. A porcupine survived 22 minutes of immersion. But the oddest experiment was done on a marmot. When its brain and spinal cord were removed, its heart continued beating for 10 hours. But a problem arises here. How do animals which sleep so deeply that neither suffocation nor a surgical operation awakes them, manage to wake up on their own? The likeliest explanation is that when the functions of the heart and lungs are slowed down as much as possible, and all the surplus fat has been consumed, the body temperature falls and the animal wakes up. If it did not wake it would probably die of cold.

If you meet a bear in winter when it should normally be hibernating, be careful. It means it has exhausted its fat reserves and woken early intending to eat an abundant meal before returning to 'sleep'.

Some spiders hibernate and hermetically seal their lairs with silken covers. Other spiders remain without food for several months but stay awake. These incredible faculties which are denied to man are perhaps the real 'magic' of animals. But who is the magician? It is Nature which has constructed a varied and complicated fresco, which will continue to hide its secret from man for ever.

Medicine

Another field in which animals are streets ahead of us is that of medicine. Man studies it for years taking difficult exams, carries out cruel and disgusting experiments, watches and possibly causes a number of people to die and attains the coveted title of 'doctor of medicine'. But animals do not 'know' anything; they do not study, nor practice but they can cure themselves efficiently on their own and often much better than we would do in a similar situation.

Some inventions which make life easier and more pleasant today have been 'suggested' to us by animals, who knew about them long before us. The application of medicinal herbs is naturally of animal origin and one which is growing today. If one thinks how long animals have lived on this earth before us, without a good number of them becoming extinct, it is evident they know how to look after themselves. All primitive peoples have brought their own kinds of therapy up to date, based on animal examples. After observing the habits of apes. Africans learned that to speed up healing their wounds, they should expose them to the sun for a long time. The stag which is wounded by the hunter and manages to escape, will drag himself to the nearest marsh and sink in it, remaining still for two days and two nights, aware through some mysterious knowledge that the medicinal property of stagnant water restores his life and vitality.

Ancient writers and illustrators were much occupied by animal medicine which came from the goat, the bear and the sheep. The hippopotamus is probably the inventor of blood-letting. When its limbs feel weak or its head feels heavy it will dash itself against some sharp rocks so that its blood will run. Aristotle was convinced that we owe this useful medical cure to the hippo. The stork would not exist as the source of a cure if it were not for Hippocrates, the most famous doctor of antiquity, who invented and applied enemas for the first time. Walking by the sea-shore one day, he saw a stork filling its beak with water and then putting it into its anal aperture. Hippocrates realised that this operation was useful to effectively evacuate its bowels. Acting on this, he did not hesitate to use it on his patients. Witch doctors in West Africa have learned much from the medical devices of animals. Observing that hippos, boars and many other wild animals would stay for a long time in rich clay puddles curing themselves of skin diseases, they put it into practice and began to cure themselves in a similar way, obtaining very good results.

It was from animals that the American Indians learned the first elements of medicine, noting which plants they looked for when they were suffering from wounds, fevers, or intestinal disturbances. The bear scrapes around to get at the roots of ferns, wild turkeys make their young eat the aromatic leaves of wintersweet during rainy periods and if wolves are bitten by a rattlesnake they chew the roots of serpentaria.

In Chile, the natives have discovered a good cure for diseases of the liver from oxen. A shepherd noticed they picked out accurately the leaves of the plant called Boldoa fragrans, when they were unwell. When he tried it himself, the shepherd discovered that the plant put the liver into perfect order. Artichokes were discovered in more or less the same way by the ancient Romans who originally used them not as food but exclusively for therapeutic ends. One of the Greek healers, Aesculapius' disciples, Dicoride, attributes the discovery of laurel, which is used for contusions and muscular pains, to doves. He saw them medicate their own ill parts with leaves plucked from the laurel tree. Foxes, according to Cicero, cured themselves of indigestion by eating rue. That is why we find it in bottles of Grappa today as an excellent digestive. Quinine, too, to which we owe so many lives, was discovered by animals. A group of wild beasts was seen dying in a Peruvian forest. They dragged themselves towards a pool of water where they chewed a plant from which a type of bitter juice came which the animals drank avidly and which gave them back their strength.

How is it that animals do not stop because of the horrible taste of a substance? How does their infallible instinct tell them that this horrible mixture will cure them? Not only are animals able to discover horrible mixtures but pleasurable things too. We will omit honey, but there is another substance whose discovery we must thank goats for, and that is coffee. In the sixteenth century in Arabia, somebody observed that after jumping about happily for some time, goats would fall exhausted to the ground. After a while they got up and went to strip red berries from a shrub and became as sprightly as before. Opium was certainly discovered by some animals who were unaware of its properties until they went to lie down happily in a field of poppies.

We are on the point of having to admit that nearly all our remedies have been discovered by animals before us, and that it is only thanks to them that we are able to look after ourselves today.

But there are still more cures which we owe to the instinct of animals. There are, for example, the undeniable precursors of hydrothermal cures. Animals which were afflicted by intestinal illnesses discovered the virtues of medicinal waters, giving man a precious gift indeed. All the beneficial waters of spring and undiscovered fountains meant nothing for man until they were discovered by oxen, horses and other animals who took themselves off to drink there, guided by a mysterious force.

One episode, among many, binds the animal world with hydrothermal cures for man. I want to refer to the account by Guiglielmo Bonuzzi in his book *L'animal questo sconosciuto* – 'This Unknown Animal'. He tells a story which is famous in Spanish Galicia where the curative virtues of hydrotherapeutics and spas were discovered in a strange way. On an island called La Toja a short distance from the Atlantic Coast, almost hidden in an inlet, a peasant once abandoned his old donkey, which had taken a turn for the worse. He did not have the courage to kill it but neither did he have enough food for an extra mouth which was giving him nothing in return. Some weeks later, stricken by remorse, the peasant returned to the spot to see what condition his donkey was in, convinced that he would find it dead. But when he saw it, he was hugely and pleasantly surprised. Not only was the donkey not dead but he was more lively and active than he had ever seen him before, and had changed colour. At first the peasant believed it was a miracle; then, seeing the donkey was brown coloured and encrusted in mud, he understood the truth. The donkey had discovered by himself the thermal properties of the muddy puddles that existed all over the island and had prescribed himself an intensive mud cure which had put him back on his feet.

Here, we must make one important distinction between medicine and surgery. Surgery is really one of man's greatest conquests which animals could never achieve. I doubt that even the most intelligent animal would know how to diagnose an ulcer or tumour, or how to operate on it. But this is the only field in which animals have not been able to act on their own. If it is wounded, every animal knows which remedy it needs for its wound. It can cure itself better than a doctor can, because it is guided by that faculty which never makes a mistake and instinct which is the most infallible in the world. Many animals seem to know and accept this.

One day a naturalist found himself in a forest and heard a demented mewing close at hand. He turned round and saw a puma, with its face horribly swollen and an air of atrocious suffering about it. The animal came towards him as if asking for help and the naturalist examined him, not without some trepidation, because being a species of large cat, the puma has a rather difficult temperament. The poor beast was suffering a lot: one of his sharpest teeth had perforated his tongue which had become swollen and he could not get it off. Obviously it was impossible for him to eat in these conditions and the infection would spread inexorably if not treated soon. But the animal knew man was able to do something for him and he remained still throughout a very painful operation giving no sign of wishing to run away or even to maul the man who was making him suffer. When the operation was over, the puma went off with a purring sound which must have meant 'thank you'.

If the puma had only been suffering from a sore paw or a bullet wound, he would not have looked for man or allowed him to help him.

A man who studied wild animals all his life was Archibald Rutledge. He has given us several examples of what excellent doctors animals are. Among animals he had was a white-tailed fawn. One day, the barbed wire of an enclosure tore the creature's side. Rutledge cleaned the wound with a carbolic solution and bandaged it up. But his patient tore off the bandage and licked the wound clean taking away all the skin and hair and exposing it to the air and the sun. He cured himself completely and was soon well.

An orang-outang or a gorilla which is wounded will try and stop the flow of blood with its hands and then cover the wound with wads of aromatic and astringent leaves. How the gorilla knows about the properties of such leaves and which ones will cure him remains a total mystery. One could deduce you can stop the flow of blood with your hands, you could also know that clay dissolves in water through experience, but astringent leaves have no particular signs of their own which distinguish them – perhaps it is the smell? But are some smells more astringent than others? Instinct is 'magical' as always.

Animals can undertake some elementary surgical operations on their own without recourse to man. Rutledge says that he once kept a flying squirrel in a huge cage. One night the creature got its paw stuck in a crack and in its frantic struggle to get free, fractured it. For many days the animal lay there with its paw in the same position. When a wild animal gets ill the first thing it does is to retire into complete solitude. Then when it has scrupulously medicated the external wound, it attempts an internal cure. It can make itself vomit and almost certainly takes a laxative.

When cats and dogs are unwell or physically suffer they eat grass. Animals with a fever will seek out a well-aired, shady place near water and remain there quietly eating little and drinking often. But in contrast, an animal suffering from rheumatism will look for the sun and absorb as much heat as it can because it alleviates the pain.

The only animal that has ever been seen undertaking a complete surgical operation was a polecat. It had got its tail caught in a trap and was wriggling about desperately to get free. Seeing it could not do it, it made the heroic decision to sacrifice its tail for its life. Little by little and with enormous strength and courage, half fainting from pain, it managed to amputate the part of its tail which was caught in the trap by biting it off. Courage won the day and at the end it fell exhausted and bleeding to the ground, with only a stump left for a tail, but alive and free.

After life, freedom is the most precious thing for an animal and this sometimes stretches beyond life.

CVLTIVATORS · SLAVES · SOLDIERS

CHAPTER 15

Cultivators, Slaves and Soldiers

I knew that sooner or later I would have to speak about ants. Their programmed, futuristic society fascinates me, even though there are some deviationary aspects. But there are positive aspects such as cultivation and breeding so we will occupy ourselves with those creatures which make us yearn to live in a similar society.

Producing and cultivating the food necessary to satisfy hunger is another of the affinities between man and animals. It is not just a matter of gathering nuts and berries as the squirrel or the woodpecker does and hoarding them until winter. It is more complicated because it implies the notion of development and yield. While a nut is always equal in that it will be the same nut in 3 months' time as today, the fungus that grows will be different in 3 months' time from the spore of today. There are not many animals which have reached this level of perception — only ants and termites — and it is well worthwhile studying their customs and practices. Some ants cultivate fungi which they feed on, but encounter a measure of difficulty in doing so because this type of fungus needs such perfect climatic conditions that even scientists have rarely been able to produce them in a laboratory.

Other species of ants have discovered the use of manure and collect the faeces of grubs, maggots and caterpillars which they use as a fertiliser in their fungus cultivation. Other insects use the skeletons of insects in the same way. The fields and gardens in cultivation are under the constant supervision of the gardener ants. Harvester ants gather grain and seed which, when shelled, is kept until winter in special underground chambers. Honey ants, instead, have devised a dazzingly cruel method of preserving honey in a way in which it can always be ready at hand. They store it in living jars. These jars are none other than the worker ants which are constrained to live below ground, hanging from the ceiling of their cells. They continually receive honey from other worker ants and regurgitate it when the community needs it. The ants which store the honey become so full that if they fall down, they burst. They therefore have every advantage, if you can talk of advantages at this level of existence, in remaining in the position assigned to them. It is sad to think that even the so-called civilisation of ants is similar to man's in its slavery and exploitation.

How much more civilised are wasps, therefore, which build small jars in which to store their honey. Ants on the other hand, are so greedy that they abandon themselves to the pleasures of gluttony, and are ready to sacrifice many of their companions to satisfy it. When they come across the grub of the large English Blue Butterfly, they drag it to their anthills where a somewhat strange exchange takes place. The grub which, until now has been vegetarian, suddenly becomes carnivorous when it grows to a length of 1 centimetre, and begins to search for insects to eat. Ants know this and allow it to eat a quantity of their own larva but in exchange they obtain a sweet, sticky substance from the grub which is a tasy titbit for them. Ants are prepared to sacrifice a whole colony of their larvae for this sweet and sticky liquid without any real need because when ants could well do with extra nourishment in winter, the grub is hibernating and it is impossible to milk them.

Apart from these grubs, ants also have 'cows' which they breed. These are small green insects like greenfly and blackfly (aphides) whose secretions contain enough amino-acids and carbohydrates to provide a complete meal for ants. The life of ants and aphides are interdependent and advantageous to both, because while the ants extract their nourishment from the greenfly, the aphides are maintained and protected against their enemies which would devour them instead of just exploiting them as the ants do. Ants keep their 'cows' in model underground barns and collect their eggs to ensure continuous breeding. In springtime, the 'calves' are taken out to pasture to graze on the buds of marguerite flowers and are watched over by herdsmen ants It is not yet known whether any sheepdog ants are involved in this activity too, but we cannot rule out that possibility.

Ant life is conditioned enormously by the natural development of the aphides. It is now accepted that aphides which are raised by ants are better off than those which are brought up in a wild state, and it is probable that this second type of aphide will shortly become extinct.

Termites cultivate fungi as well, but with completely different objectives in view from ants. Termite fungi grow on a base which is specially prepared and composed of finely crumbled wood. For a long time it was thought that the function of this fungus was to predigest the wood and split the cellulose to transform it into digestible sugar. But recent studies have thrown light on a much stranger reason. The part of the wood that the fungus makes digestible is not the cellulose but a very hard substance called lignin which is much more difficult to change than cellulose. As the wood is digested by the fungus, the termites gradually clear it away, immediately substituting fresh wood on which the fungus can carry out its destructive work. The fungus itself is never eaten by the termites.

Soldiers and Slaves

Ant societies have an incredible similarity with the Nazi régime. They practice genocide and infanticide and select the race with warlike and colonial objectives in mind. Some species select individuals gifted with robust jaws and designate them as soldiers. The selection is made according to their various capacities and is so rigid and strong that a hunter ant will not lift a finger to do the work of another ant even if it is easy and trivial. All ants are warlike but ants in South America and Africa literally live for war. Their enormous armies attack any animal and if the enemy is another group of ants, the adversaries are taken prisoner and made into slaves.

Deviationist as it may seem, sociologists and psychologists are agreed that a society which practices slavery is more evolved than a society which has never even conceived of the idea. Naturally the ideal would be to know about slavery and its advantages but not to practise it, but such a society, which would be decidedly utopian for animals, has not yet been discovered. When we witness the liberation of slave ants by the bloodthirsty warrior ants we will really be able to say that ant society functions much better than human society. The warrior ant, commonly known as the red ant, is found in three continents, Asia, Europe and America. Periodically its bellicose armies attack the anthills of the black ant and then possess the larva which they then breed with great care and diligence.

This is effectively a watered-down slavery, seeing that once they are adult the 'slaves' lead the same life as the other ants, with similar rights and similar duties. This enlightened slavery has its origins in the behaviour of the young queen who is incapable of founding a new colony on her own after her nuptial flight, and searches for a ready-made nest which, of necessity, is already inhabited. The queen ant takes command of several larvae, killing those who oppose her. From these larvae, 'subject' ants are born while the larvae and ants, belonging to the queen, retain a liking for brigandesque raids.

With Amazonian ants, slavery is different. Gifted with tremendous jaws, they can cut off the enemy's head with one blow. The slaves here are always the black ants and take on the rôle of slaves and are the servants of those they serve. Termite society has a military character, too, and an enormously important place is held by the army within the many castes it is divided into. It is so perfectly structured that you almost expect to meet termites with their rank on their sleeves.

CHAPTER 16

Raffles, the Patriotic Talking Bird

For anyone who has heard a mynah bird talk, the story about Raffles, the most famous talking bird in the world, is incredible. These fantastic birds have been known and appreciated for their true worth for only a short while and when they have been taught to speak their price is prohibitive.

A few years ago, when mynah birds were not so well known, an American millionaire wanted to give his mother a present. She lived far away and he just did not know what to choose. He had already given her houses, jewels, furs, cars, paintings, everything, yet that Christmas he was short of ideas. Finally a friend of his suggested a talking mynah bird. It cost the millionaire quite a lot of money but it was an original idea and would keep her company. Enthused by the idea, the magnate acquired one of the best-trained talkers and a cage, equipped with every comfort, and sent it with every precaution to his mother, accompanied by a card.

After a while, amazed at not receiving rapturous thanks, he telephoned his mother and having paid her the usual compliments and inquiries about her health, he asked: "Well, mother, did you like the mynah bird I sent you for Christmas?"

"Oh yes, dear," replied his mother, "it was delicious and so tender."

Fortunately, it would be difficult for a mynah bird to run a similar risk today and end up in the oven. They are becoming so sought-after that many elegant houses are now decorated with these birds as if they were superb pieces of luxury furniture. It needs time and patience to teach them to talk but the results are worth the trouble. And what is more a mynah bird can link what it is saying with thought, especially if it is about something which affects it personally.

This is the story of a mynah bird called Raffles which was adopted by Carveth and Zetta Wells. One night in 1939 they were camping on an island off Malaya when the silence of the jungle was broken by a high-pitched squawking. A snake in search of its prey had slithered up a tree and captured a sleeping bird. The following morning the couple discovered the scene of the crime. Black feathers were scattered at the foot of a tall tree and about 9 metres above them, the head of a small bird with its beak wide open poked out from a hollow in the tree. Ali, their Malaysian guide, climbed up the tree and brought the small derelict bird to safety. It was ugly, all beak and no feathers, except for a few black ones which were broken off. Ali told them it was an intelligent bird which would be able to talk when it had grown. And that was how Raffles came into their possession.

When they took him home, the customs officer examined their declaration closely and asked them what kind of bird it was.

"It's a talking bird," Zetta replied.

The customs man wrinkled his nose. "We don't allow parrots to come in, they carry diseases," he said.

"It's not a parrot, it's a mynah bird," the Wells explained. It was a cold day and Zetta was carrying the bird under her fur coat. She took it out and perched him on her finger. His feathers were ruffled because it was a cold day. He stared at the customs man and said in a cordial and captivating tone "Hello Joe". Joe had been the name of their waiter on board ship and fortunately it was the name of the customs officer also. He was absolutely astounded. "How does he know my name?" he said. "That's not a parrot, that's a mind reader. All right then, through you go."

Mynah birds are common in Asia and can imitate man's speech to perfection. They are different from parrots and can copy the exact tone and inflection of their master's voice. They can imitate nearly every sound.

Raffles was black with shining feathers, except for two small white blobs on his wings. His beak was bright orange. At three months he could say "Hello darling", using the same affectionate voice as Zetta. Every time he saw her prepare food, he would say with live anticipation in his voice "What a beauty". It was not long before he called them both by name. He also imitated Carveth's mother and Carveth would often reply until he suddenly realised it was Raffles.

Many people forget that mynahs are capable of thinking. If Raffles wanted a bunch of grapes he would say, "I want a grape". When the tap was turned on to fill the bath, Raffles shouted, "I want a bath", but if it was only the kitchen tap, he would say nothing. Raffles always shouted "Hello, hello" whenever the telephone rang and once, when Zetta was out, Carveth made her talk to Raffles on the phone. He listened attentively for a while, then called Zetta and, not seeing her appear, pecked the receiver furiously.

One day when Sarah Churchill was staying with the Wells in New York, a friend of hers telephoned and asked for Tony, Sarah's husband. "Tony is in California," said Sarah "and I am alone in New York." At that very moment, Raffles, who was nearby, exclaimed "Hello darling" in a deep masculine voice. "I thought you were alone," said the friend. "Who is that?"

"I am alone," protested Sarah, "except for Raffles who is a bird." The voice was so human that Sarah had to invite her friend over to see Raffles for himself.

A radio comedian, Fred Allen, set Raffles on the path to stardom by including him in his radio programme. The mynah bird gave an extraordinary performance and surprising offers of work began to pour in. He appeared on several programmes and in Hollywood many film stars hurried to see him. Walt Disney was so enchanted that he offered a meal in his honour. *Time* magazine, commenting on his success said: "Hollywood has found an extraordinary new comedian with no rivals. It is a bird with an orange beak, named Raffles who says the most opportune things at the most opportune times."

The mynah's greatest triumph was to have a solo part written for him with the San Francisco Symphony Orchestra during a festival to celebrate the orchestra's thirty-third anniversary. About 12,000 people crowded into the immense civic auditorium and Zetta, with Raffles on her wrist, placed herself in the middle of the enormous stage. Until that day, Raffles had never seen so many strange objects like drums, cellos and trumpets. Although he eyed the objects suspiciously, there was no need to worry. In the 5 minutes that followed, Raffles held the immense public open-mouthed with admiration. When he finished his programme, whistling the national anthem, the applause was deafening.

In 1943 it was decided that Raffles should dedicate all his time to the war effort and he sold war bonds to the value of 15 million dollars, and received a decoration for having entertained wounded troops in military hospitals. Raffles had scarcely finished his tenth show in a naval hospital when a woman, red-eyed with much crying, came up to Zetta and said, "My son is going to die. He has heard Raffles on the radio and when he knew Raffles was coming to the hospital, he said the thing he most wanted in the world was that bird."

Scarcely had Carveth gone into the boy's room than he felt his heart strings tighten. A rubber tube was attached to the boy's nose and wound like a snake over the bedcovers. The bird had never seen a snake before but mynahs take fright at anything resembling them. The vacuum-cleaner tube was enough to make him fly off squawking in fear. But by some mysterious instinct, which always made this extraordinary bird undertake the right course of actions, Raffles flew down on to the arm of the dying boy, and said in a caressing tone, "Hello love". The boy started and the bird began to whistle a tune. The doctor turned his back and the nurse began to cry. But the mother's face was transfigured with joy. When her son looked at Raffles he recognised him and smiled. He died that night.

Nobody ever thought that Raffles would die as well. One day during a performance in a military hospital in New York, Raffles caught a cold. That night, he began to cough and sneeze. The next morning he could not even manage to speak or whistle but continued murmuring "Poor Raffles, poor Raffles" over and over again. He was attended day and night for a week, but even the care of the vet and the aviarist could not save him. He was 8 years old when he died. Today, his body lies in the American Museum of Natural History.

This story is moving and true. All these beautiful animal stories with happy endings should be preserved like rare wines so that our small and faithful friends would never leave us and would continue to undertake their miracles. But for this to happen we would have to live in a fairy tale and not the real world.

Animals are born, grow up, make us happy with a thousand small marks of affection and then die before we do, leaving a void which comes as a horrible injustice. If I could express one desire about animals, I would wish that every animal could live as its owner, or the person it likes best in the world. There is a 'magic' about animals, which have the capacity of making themselves an important and recognised member of the family. I refer only to those families who really love animals and not those who keep animals for a specific use such as a guard-dog or a hunting dog.

Every time I try and put my cats into harness to carry them through the traffic safely, they plant themselves firmly like stakes in the ground and categorically refuse to move. No ham, prawns or cheese will tempt them to move, and these are foods they are crazy about. This is called 'character' and because of this, whatever their action is acquires value because it happens spontaneously and is done to 'please'.

ANIMAL·LANGUAGE

bee dancing

CHAPTER 17

Animal Language and Birdsong

A book on animal language was published some years ago by Bill Gilbert. It was called *The Language of Animals*. I will not dwell on it for long but want to examine briefly the more particular language of dance and smell. Some animal languages which are incomprehensible to us, can be extremely suggestive, even more so than human language. But everyone has his language. The language of dance is splendid but could we do it without appearing ridiculous? The love-dance of the speckled fish or of elegant birds has a grace which only a great ballerina could imitate.

Bees also speak through dance. Their language was studied thoroughly by the famous zoologist, Von Frisch, who has contributed so much to ethology. Bees dance to convey a message, to tell the rest of their swarm that they have found a plate with interesting titbits on it, to indicate the right direction and to let them know the exact distance.

Von Frisch has ascertained that the speed of what he calls this 'vibration dance' indicates the exact distance in hundreds of metres as to where the food has been discovered. One dance giration, completed in 1.5 seconds, tells the bees that the food is about 100 metres away. The same giration, completed in 2 seconds signifies 200 metres and so on. In bee language, there are dialectical and national differences and an Italian bee will find it difficult to understand an

Australian bee which uses different measurements of distance.

Bees are not disposed to dance to express the concept of 'up there'. This is understandable because nothing exists in nature which is so high that it cannot easily be seen by a bee. It is man who has invented towers and skyscrapers and bees have not yet learned to dominate them.

Bees use the water-dance to tell their companions it is too hot in the hive and that they need some liquid nectar or pure water. There is also the dance of the explorer bees which tells the others they have found a new location for the beehive. When the explorer bees have found a new place, each group executes a propaganda dance on behalf of the place it considers best. An experimenter once counted over twenty-one places which bees had to decide between to build their new beehive. Unanimity is a must in these decisions and if no agreement is reached, after many days' discussion, the bees build the hive on any branch and renounce the sheltered recess they need. Bee language is hereditary since they do not learn it as young bees but are born with methods of communicating which they use later on as adults. This does not mean bees cannot learn anything new or elaborate on what they already know.

Birds, as we know, communicate with their voice, and not always with song. Lorenz even managed to speak to some of them, carefully using their sounds. Everyone must remember his famous conversations with the female goose, Martina, based on 'vivivivivi' and 'gangangangan'.

All birds speak in their own way and with some patience you can learn the language of many of them, if you rid yourself of the preconceived notion that birds 'sing' for the same motives that we do, to express joy, love or other pleasurable sentiments.

Birds can produce beautiful songs for absolutely banal reasons – to be recognised, to raise the alarm or to tell the time. Their personal feelings are expressed in far less charming ways and their vocabulary is far less rich than other animals. Even birds which talk the best are not the most garrulous.

The cricket, for example, uses sixteen signals compared with the twenty-two of chickens. This is the maximum number of vocal signals that birds can achieve.

If you add visuals to this, such as showing off plumage, you get a vocabulary of thirty to forty signals. But there is no universal language among birds – it varies from species to species and even between those of the same species living in different places. Naturally, all birds possess danger signals, noises for calling their young and others of identification. There are also territorial songs which males use to define the boundaries of their territory. Courting is not always expressed by song alone but with gestures and by other means.

Another particular language is that of the butterfly which expresses itself chiefly through smell. Smell is indissolubly linked with shapes and colours and serves the completely mute butterfly as a summons across several miles and can also discourage an enemy by emitting destructive odours.

The fox can call its cubs without making a sound: just by looking at them. Rabbits and certain rodents communicate by Morse code thumping the ground gently, which their opposite numbers interpret as signs of alarm or messages of anger. Does warn their young of danger by raising their tails and showing the white part underneath, while elephants express themselves by waving their trunks and ears. Ants can talk from one tree to another by hitting the bark of the tree with their legs, obtaining a sound rather like the patter of raindrops. Many fish, which have long believed to be mute, let out sounds which are perfectly clear to their own species. Dolphins, on the other hand, talk mostly in whistles and will soon be able to talk to us if experiments continue. In a while we might break the great barrier that divides us from our brother animals.

Talking of summons, the strangest, most beautiful and suggestive is the scintillating 'speech' of the glow worm. No one can fail to have been ecstatic, when they were small, at seeing this tiny dancing light and incredulous at finding it in such tiny bodies which were not plugged in or run from batteries. The glow worm can produce the most perfect kind of light which man has never discovered – light without heat. By night it acquires all its splendour, but a glow worm seen in the day is a brownish insignificant insect. The European glow worm is tiny but in the West Indies where everything assumes enormous proportions, the same coleoptera, known as 'cucuyos' are much larger and so bright that natives attach them to their bare legs to light the way.

In Brazil, girls put glow worms in their hair and there is nothing more enchanting than to see these tiny darting lights intertwined in their curly locks. This romantic light is a precise sexual summons for a glow worm and has been perfectly deciphered. The male emits its light every 5.8 seconds to signify it is looking for a female. The female which is generally hidden in the grass, signals her reply by emitting a light every 2.1 seconds after receiving the male's call. So there is no danger of the male confusing a male with a female light even though their colour is identical. He follows her replies in a docile fashion until they are united in the shade. There are other kinds of glow worms for whom light is not a sexual call and who only shine in their larval or egg form.

What is this strange light used for then? If it is not to cheer up the summer nights, then we have no answer as yet. It is not for their defence, since it would show them up to their enemy, nor is it to light the way because the light is placed on the hind part of the body. In fact, one could believe that, just for once, nature has given us something free which approaches absolute beauty.

The old saying 'silent as a fish' is false especially as many beliefs are based upon superficial observation. Nobody pretends that fish sing or shout, bark or mew, but they do make sounds. Ichthyologists have made long studies and have discovered that fish cannot let out vocal sounds similar to our own because of their bronchial breathing. But in compensation they can emit characteristic sounds stimulated by joy or sadness, which are attributed to the opercula, the jawbones or the teeth. The tuna fish emits a touching whimper like a newborn babe when it is captured. There is a creature which is a cross between a fish and amphibia and which hisses like a snake if it is maltreated. The moonfish grunts and gurgles. The drumfish gives out very strange sounds and Darwin tells of a fish which lives in the Argentinian Sea and which lets out a harsh, angry sound if it gets caught on a fish hook.

In fact, the underwater world is not as silent as we imagine. It is run through with an infinite number of sounds, some perceptible to the human ear, others not. We have already seen that even though they are not fish, cetaceans live in the sea and contribute enormously with their whistles and imitations of human voices. It has been ascertained that nearly all fish can let out ultrasonic sounds, some of which have been recorded. The day when we understand what the sounds mean may not be far away.

Fish are certainly unlucky in not being able to talk. They have much less chance of being able to soften the heart of the human beast who is exterminating them mercilessly. An animal that cannot whimper or cry, has no other way of defending itself other than a desperate struggle to free itself, which often does no more than excite its captor, and does not generally move anyone to pity; small soft mammals with intelligent eyes which seem to appeal to the heart and the pity of those who are about to kill them, or a bird which shrieks and chirps can sometimes move the hunter to pity. Two episodes I remember well because they happened to me and people close to me, I will now recount.

When my grandmother was young, hunting was considered a very elegant activity (I refuse to call it a sport) for women: it was an occasion to dress up and a chance to make sporty, elegant clothes and go on lovely walks in the woods followed by unforgettable picnics with one's friends. Though a good person, my grandfather was, alas, also a great hunter and one day my grandmother decided to copy him. She made herself an extremely elegant hunting dress and very sure of herself, because she was a woman with a strong character, left with a gun in her hands and accompanied them. When the moment came she sighted a bird, took aim and fired. The bird was not hit but frightened by the shot and let out such a heartrending chirruping that my grandmother did something, which still happened to women in the early days of this century, she fell to the ground in a dead faint. It was her first and last hunt. There is an episode which still makes me laugh even though it happened several years ago. I have always hated hunting, hunters and especially those who maintain they love animals, and all those who in some way harm animals when there is no legitimate case of self defence. At 4 years old with all the force of desperation, I took on a little boy who was older than me, biting and kicking him because he was torturing a grasshopper by pulling off first its wings, then its legs and then its antennae. I wanted to tell this to show that I have always loved and defended animals.

One day at the seaside when I was seven I was overcome with the desire to fish. I considered fish less 'animals' than others. So armed with my small fishing rod and seated on a rock, I began my great enterprise. After a while there was a little tug at the rod and a fish got hooked. Excited, I pulled at it and that was the end. When I saw the fish wriggle in spasms and look at me with those unexpectedly expressive and imploring eyes, I burst into desperate tears and begged my friends to save it. The fish was taken off the hook and thrown back into the water. I do not know whether it survived, but at least that terrible feeling that I was an assassin disappeared.

A lady I knew had a fish which she understood perfectly. It would tell her if its food was all right, whether it was in a good mood or angry (in which case it became all red) and it swam forward whenever she came near the aquarium. When science has discovered the secret of the underwater world, fish will no longer be gracious ornaments in a tank but agreeable domesticated animals like many others.

There are some animals which are much easier to love because of their grace, their beauty and their intelligence; while others are more difficult, and demand much patience, trust and optimism. But in the end, they give enormous satisfaction. It is relatively easy to teach a dog to carry a newspaper but would it not be much more interesting, for example, to teach a large wasp to bring a pencil or some other small object and fly over with it. I don't believe that I could ever manage to domesticate a spider and make friends with it but Silvio Pellico did. Abundant time, solitude and above all a great and inexhaustible supply of patience can achieve miracles with animals. I have gone off at a tangent from my discourse on fish and their sounds: perhaps I feel rather guilty towards them.

Bird song

Without a doubt birds are some of nature's most pleasing products. They are a pleasure whether you just look at them or just listen to them. The variations in their song can be imitated but never reproduced. Their melodies are infinite. Looking at the argument in a more scientific way, let us see what the notable ornithologist, Professor Janos Szoeke has to say. In 1960, the Professor, who learned well over two thousand different tunes from the lark, published the results of his work on the mystery of bird-song. He declared the lark to have absolute supremacy among birds gifted with a sense of music. The skylark beats the nightingale hands down in inventiveness and the incredible intensity of its tonal scale. If the nightingale has the talent of virtuosity, the skylark possesses the creativity of a composer. The melody that flows from its fine beak presents, under analysis, a finesse of construction and mastery of the superior craft that one finds in simple popular music.

Szoeke was not talking conjecturally; he analysed the quality and composition of the lark's song with great care and stated that the extraordinary passerines succeeded in emitting, in the trill of 1 second, one hundred and thirty different notes. Naturally, the human ear is not adapted to capturing the shadings of this scale which bursts forth with such richness.

An ornithologist has been able to establish mathematically the number of notes sung by a lark in 1 second after recording its song on a tape recorder. He then slowed down the speed by one sixteenth in relation to its normal speed, and natural duration and continued in successive recordings to gradually slow down sounds that had already been slowed down to analyse in the space of 100 hours, all the elementary notes in the song. This explanation is perhaps rather too technical, but those who understand even a little bit of music will be able to appreciate the results of this great student.

It seems that as with the animals we have seen which taught man his medicine, so it is with music and man has begun to learn from birds. Certainly, man has tried to learn and imitate the prodigious song of the birds and when he did not succeed, concentrated his efforts with considerable results into creating masterpieces we all know. Beethoven, for instance, a sensitive and grateful person, acknowledged the supremacy of birds by inserting the song of the chaffinch into his 'Pastoral Symphony'. Many poets and musicians have praised bird-song, including it in their works. Among them are d'Annunzio, Maupassant and Puccini. Many others have sought to imitate birds and many have conquered this difficulty but have never reproduced it. Bird-song is another of nature's great pieces of 'magic'. Man can do almost everything, but he cannot create what nature does and perhaps he never will.

CHAPTER 18

Wise Animals: Horses and Dogs

It has always been known that dogs are some of the most intelligent of creatures, but false beliefs also surround them, which often considerably diminish their repute.

Konrad Lorenz has thrown light on several points from experiments he has done with his own dogs.

Dogs descend either from the *Canis aureus* (golden jackal) or the *Canis lupus* (northern wolf). According to Lorenz, who is a great champion of the wolf, the latter are more faithful and mature than dogs, and always love one single master and are more independent characters. The aureus, however, he says, is more childish and playful, submissive and easily domesticated. A perfect sample can be had by crossing the two races, whose descendants then have the best qualities of both. Lorenz proved the falsity of the commonly-held belief that dogs understand the intonation but not the sense of phrases. Let us see what he says about this in his book *And Man Met Dog*.

"It is a great mistake to believe that dogs only understand the meaning of a word from the intonation of the voice and remain deaf to its actual articulation.

"A well-known student of animal psychology, Sarris, showed this in a reliable way through his experiments on three sheepdogs called Harris, Aris and Paris. If their owner said 'Harris (or Aris or Paris) go to bed', the named dog would unfailingly get up and go sadly but obediently towards his kennel. The experiment worked even when the command came from an adjoining room and there was, therefore, no possibility of a gesture however involuntary."

We cannot speak of knowledgeable animals without referring to the famous 'reasoning of dogs' of Mannheim. It is a real shame that the fashion for making these experiments on the intellectual faculties of animals has died down; today, we hardly ever hear of them at all and so we have to rely on those carried out many years ago and which still evoke the same interest today as yesterday.

There was an Airedale terrier called Rolf who belong to a Mrs. Moekel and who lived with a puppy called Jela and a cat called Daisy. I should mention in passing that the puppy learned to reproduce the sounds of the human word and could distinctly say 'Mamma' and other words, while the cat was able to solve mathematical problems.

But the most interesting protagonist, and the one which excited the most discussion, was Rolf. Mackenzie, in an essay published in the review *Psyche* described him as 'happy, good and above all sincere; very sensitive to affection and capable of returning it also; he is extremely sensitive to blame and to praise'. This is as far as sentiments are concerned; for the other attributes, he noted in his summary: strong memory, an extremely fine sense of hearing and good sight but a weak sense of smell.

At 3 years old, Rolf could work out square roots and would often help Mrs. Moekel's sons with their homework. To talk, he used a counting frame and answered in a Mannheim dialect even if he was questioned in literary German.

Rolf gave far more importance to sounds than to 'writing' and even had his own form of shorthand. He studied with the small Moekel boy and learned geography, grammar and other subjects with him. His syntax was perfect and he never forgot to use verbs which is often a common defect among talking animals, ignoramuses and people trying to learn a foreign language.

On June 24, 1913, in the presence of four scholars who had come from Heidelberg to study the phenomen, Mrs. Moekel asked Rolf to construct a phrase using an adjective. The dog was tired and did not want to do it. Finally, he constructed a phrase which expressed his state of mind exactly. "The mistress is wicked and the master very good." Rolf was perfectly conscious of his extraordinary faculties and considered himself far more human than animal. This was proved one day in an amusing and indicative episode. In German 'to eat' can be said in two ways: 'essen' which refers to man and 'fressen' which refers to animals. Noting that when he spoke about himself Rolf would always use the verb 'essen', he was asked one day to use the verb 'fressen' and replied saying it applied to mules.

I have already spoken about his sense of humour: he could pull people's legs and tease them too. Once Mrs. Moekel was referring to Rolf's denigrators in Mannheim and asked him to define these men. Rolf replied that they were asses.

At his first session with Mackenzie on September 9, 1913, Mackenzie asked Rolf to say something, anything he wanted. Rolf asked him: "Who are you?" Assured that the visitor liked dogs and had come from far away to get to know him, Rolf said: "Rolf likes you too." To the question "I know you don't like working, but what do you like doing?" Rolf, who had decidedly refined habits, replied: "Eating smoked salmon." At the end of the session, Rolf was tired and Mackenzie promised to let him finish after he had told him what he liked more than smoked salmon and which other animals would like as well. He had to choose an object which was not a comestible. Rolf shut his eyes and thought for a bit and then replied 'paintings'.

At the September 20th session, Rolf recognised Mr. Mackenzie, his questioner from the previous session, and repeated his name. Then an experiment was carried out using four cards of different designs but the same size which proved that the conscious or even unconscious communication between the dog and those present was impossible. Rolf recognised the designs on the cards perfectly. None of those present could have transmitted what was on the cards because they were mixed up and only the dog could see them. When he was shown the picture of a basset hound and asked what it was, he replied: "A basset hound." To the question "Are you a basset hound?" he replied: "I am a dog."

He then explained that the difference between himself and a basset hound lay in the fact that he preferred ladies to young men, because they had long hair and beautiful clothes and that the major difference between men and women was that men wore trousers. In a session on September 21, he was asked "What is autumn?" He replied: "It is the time when there are apples", revealing his aptitude for abstract thought and also expressing a concept of time. His final and most interesting reply was to the question asking him what an animal was. Rolf replied: "It is part of the universal soul."

Horses

I have not spoken much about horses until now and I will limit myself to talking about the story of the Elberfeld horses which happened many years ago and has now become a legend. The story of these horses, who are linked with the names of Wilhelm Von Osten and Karl Krall, is too well known to tell in complete detail here.

The manifestations of Krall's horses, studied by men for whom scientific problems constituted the prime reason of activities directed towards the pursuit of truth, are now incontestible. Scientists who until yesterday had seen in animals nothing more than agents of chemical and physical forces, and who maintained a rigid position of neutrality like those who will not deny a thing but neither will they allow animals the possibility of an interior life, must now bow in front of the evidence of the facts and confess, with a beautiful gesture of scientific sincerity as Ziegler, Claparede and Flournoi did, that in the presence of the demonstrations of the Elberfeld horses, they could not do other than to accord them a psychic and sufficiently evolved life.

Von Osten discovered the existence of a certain grade of intelligence in his horse, Hans, and decided to subject it to an accurate and methodical education which produced surprising results in that Hans had great success in solving mathematical problems. He used to reply by beating his hooves of his front legs on the ground using the conventional alphabet to answer questions. He accomplished the orders shouted to him without any help.

Exposed to the public gaze, Hans stupified the Berliners and excited the Imperial Press so much that an Academic Commission was set up to study this strange and unusual case. But while accepting the reality of their observations, the Commission denied Hans the faculty of thought because it believed the phenomenon it was studying resulted from slight signals coming unconsciously from Von Osten.

Mackenzie states that we owe Von Osten recognition for showing us that human thought is not a privilege of man. Other creatures until now have been held as inferior to man in spite of living beside and among us and being equivalent to us in their nobility of mind.

But several of the men on the Commission established many deficiencies of method in the Hans case and in 1908 he took up the educational experiments again using two young Arab horses – 2-year-old Muhammed and $2\frac{1}{2}$-year-old Zarif. The teaching method conceived by Krall had now been perfected since Von Osten first began. For numbers Muhammed and Zarif stamped out units with their right foreleg and tens with their left foreleg. For the letters of the alphabet, Krall used a table in which each letter was performed by tapping out a small number of blows with one or the other foot.

The mathematical instruction led to the discovery of an extraordinary and completely unexpected fact. The horses revealed they were natural, calculating prodigies. When they had learned the meaning of what they were doing, they soon showed themselves capable of accomplishing the process with much larger numbers. Muhammed, whose mathematical faculty was more highly developed than Zarif's, could subtract square root from six and seven figure numbers.

Dr. Schoeller collaborated with Krall for some time and one day wrote on the blackboard: 'What is sugar?' Muhammed beat out the word 'sweet' with his hooves. Schoeller wrote again: 'That is not a proposition, what else do you need to add?' Muhammed beat out: 'Sugar is'. Then Schoeller said: 'What else can you say about sugar?' And Muhammed beat out: 'Sugar is white.' Finally Schoeller asked: 'And what else?' And Muhammed replied: 'Sugar tastes good.'

Krall is resolute that horses can think, reason and speak. They can be taught to cope with arithmetical problems that even non-specialist adults would find difficult to do by memory in the same amount of time. Above all, horses have an interior life of their own, quite independently from any education that has been given them and which manifests itself in spontaneous, unexpected and absolutely human ways.

An attempt to instruct a horse was also made in Italy by a Dr. Ricciarelli, with Pythagorus a half breed horse of 16 months. The lessons were about 20 minutes long each and obtained good results even though they were not as exceptional as the German horses. Pythagorous learned to offer his right or left foot on request, to ask for fodder, hay and sugar respectively and to read numbers up to ten. Also he promptly obeyed any command. One conclusion that all horse instructors have in common is that the results are obtained with gentleness and rewards and never with blows or strokes.

Lorenz the great ethologist denies that horses have any reasoning faculties, attributing telepathic and perceptive faculties to them instead. This is what he writes about it: "All these counting talking and thinking animals 'speak' by knocking or barking sounds whose meaning is laid down after the fashion of a Morse code. At first sight, their performances are really astounding. You are invited to set the examination yourself and you are put opposite the horse, terrier or whatever animal it is. You ask, how much is two times two? The terrier scrutinises you intently and barks four times. In a horse the feat seems still more prodigious for he does not even look at you. In dogs, who watch the examiner closely, it is obvious that their attention is concentrated upon the latter and not by any means on the problem itself. But the horse has no need to turn his eyes towards the examiner since it can see the minutest movement in any direction even in a direction in which the animal is not directly focusing. And it is you yourself who betrays involuntarily the right solution to the 'thinking' animal. Should one not know the right answer oneself then the poor animal will knock or bark desperately waiting in vain for the sign which tells him to stop. As a rule this sign is forthcoming since few people are capable even with the utmost self control of withholding an unconscious and involuntary signal."

I want to finish with the story of a horse called Merano which won many trophies with his rider Raimondo d'Inzeo. Merano understood everything and replied in different ways according to whether gentle words or otherwise were used, even though they were pronounced in the same tone of voice. He was sweet and affectionate when he heard talk of sugar, but if his groom said in the same gentle tone, "I am going to kill you," the horse would kick furiously against the side of his box.